THE DISHWASHER MANUAL

DIY Plumbing □ Maintenance □ Repair

Graham Dixon

First edition published 1990
Revised second edition
published 1993

© Graham Dixon 1993

Published by:
Haynes Publishing Group
Sparkford, Nr Yeovil, Somerset
BA22 7JJ, England

Haynes Publishing Inc.
861 Lawrence Drive,
Newbury Park,
California 91320 USA

**British Library Cataloguing in
Publication Data**

A catalogue record for this book is
available from the British Library

ISBN 1 85010 866 8 (Book Trade)
ISBN 1 85010 867 6 (Motor Trade)

Printed in Great Britain by
J. H. Haynes & Co. Ltd.

**While every effort is taken to
ensure the accuracy of the
information given in this book, no
liability can be accepted by the
author or publishers for any loss,
damage or injury caused by errors
in, or omissions from, the
information given.**

Contents

Introduction

The repair and servicing of today's modern domestic appliances may possibly seem a daunting task to perform oneself. The myth consists of several elements:

(a) The mystique created by the manufacturers that their machines are more complicated than they actually are.

(b) The inbuilt fear of electrical wiring that most laymen seem to have (this is not a bad thing as electricity is to be respected at any voltage, and at all times when working on a machine **it must be isolated from the main supply**).

(c) The lack of detailed manuals to suit the person that can overcome 'a' and 'b'.

(d) The fact that if you get past 'a', 'b' and 'c', the parts are – in most instances – difficult to obtain.

One may be forgiven for thinking that this is a good reason for leaving the repair of your machine to someone who possesses the skills, manuals and parts. This unfortunately generally proves expensive in call-out and labour charges, often only to find that it was a five minute job, with the cost of parts £5.00, and the call-out and labour £30.00. In the customer's mind, £35.00 is little expense for such complicated and unsafe items. Yet their D.I.Y. husband (or wife) will gladly strip down the engine or brakes on their family car, and will take the family out for a drive that afternoon. It is acceptable for car repairs to be carried out by the D.I.Y. enthusiast as the information and parts are readily available. This obviously means that the D.I.Y. car owner saves a labour charge of only £10 to £15 per hour. Until now, the D.I.Y. enthusiast has been unable to repair any major faults to his dishwasher due to the manufacturers and repair companies not wishing to disclose the information. This state of affairs can be remedied by studying the following chapters, coupled with the application of a little common sense. There is now a comprehensive range of 'blister packed' spares are appearing in most good D.I.Y. chain stores, and on public market stalls. As these are manufactured for the general public, they are usually clearly marked with the type of machine and application.

We hope that this manual will be of great assistance in not only reducing your repair costs, but giving the satisfaction which is obtained when a repair is successfully completed.

This manual has been thoughtfully designed to help you understand the function and operation of the internal components of your dishwasher.

Flowcharts, diagrams and step-by-step photographic sequences have been used to attain a logical pattern to fault finding. This enables the reader to follow a sequence of events in theory (using the flowcharts), in practice (using the photographic sequences) and in detail (using the diagrams).

This manual will assist you in finding the fault and in giving you the knowledge to repair it. Another important aspect is the regular checking and maintenance of your machine, which is covered in the individual sections, and also a checklist section in Chapter 8.

We hope you will use this manual to assist you in the Do It Yourself repair of your machine. With most repairs you will find it speedier than calling a repair company, and at the same time save the added burden of call-out and labour charges that repair companies must charge to cover overheads and operating costs.

With this in mind, we hope that your faults are few and far between, but remember . . . prevention is better than cure, and regular checks and servicing of your machine can prevent any bigger problems arising into the future.

Acknowledgements

The author would like to extend his thanks and gratitude to the following people and organisations for their help in the compilation of certain sections.

He would like to thank Oracstar for their help and information that was used in the plumbing section, SUN dishwasher products (Lever Brothers) for allowing him to use sections of their various guides.

Thanks also to Andrew Morland for the photographic work.

Chapter 1

The dishwasher

Today, modern kitchens consist of many labour saving appliances, many of which we have come to look upon as essential and not merely a luxury. The automatic washing machine fits into this category along with such items as electric toasters, irons, etc. However, one major appliance, the dishwasher falls somewhere between, being a most welcome but luxury item. After its initial purchase and use however, it is regarded as being essential.

It has been calculated that for the average family of four, over 546 hours or three full weeks each year will be spent washing dishes! On these figures alone, any machine that would ease this burden on the household could hardly be classed as a luxury.

Not only is a dishwasher a labour saving appliance, it is, if kept well maintained, a very hygienic way of washing soiled dishes and eating utensils. Three main reasons for this claim are:

1. The wash temperatures are higher than can be used if washing by hand and the machine will also wash for a longer time at the higher temperature.

2. The load is then well rinsed in clear, fresh water – something rarely done when washing by hand.

3. Drying is done by heat within the machine and not by a tea towel. Tests have proved that, although many people wash their dishes clean, they then proceed to dry them with a tea towel which may transfer contamination back onto the dishes prior to them being put back into cupboards. People are now realising that the true benefits of dishwashers are not only labour saving, but also the most hygienic way of washing dishes, etc.

As with all such labour saving devices, they can be taken for granted, and regular maintenance and inspection procedures ignored, and it is only when the machine develops a fault which puts it out of action, does the owner/user realise how useful the machine really is!

Most people, including some service engineers, have little understanding of dishwashers, their operation and functions, and their particular faults and problems. In actual fact, they are not as complex as an automatic clothes washing machine, and in some instances, they have many items in common with them. As with the *Washing Machine*

Manual, this book will help you to understand the workings of your dishwasher and guide and instruct you in its repair when required. Above all, the maintenance steps will help keep the dishwasher at peak performance, and in turn will help keep faults to a minimum.

How they work

To aid in the correct usage of a dishwasher and to help with maintenance and repair, it will be necessary to fully understand the way in which they operate and carry out their functions.

Understanding the wash procedures will be of great help when diagnosing faults that may arise. The workings of a dishwasher are in principle quite simple, yet many repair engineers themselves do not fully understand them and tend to treat them as being rather complex and troublesome to repair. Their lack of confidence is often transferred to the customer and DIY repairer when obtaining spare parts. The aim in writing this manual is to give you not only the knowledge for repairing your machine, but also the confidence to do it. Dishwashers are basically much less complicated than automatic clothes washing machines although they are similar in many respects, i.e.

a. The thorough and efficient cleansing of soiled items
b. Thorough rinsing to remove all traces of wash powders
c. To dry items following the wash and rinse programmes

The main differences are:

a. It is the wash water under pressure that is moved OVER the pots (unlike the clothes washer where clothes are agitated through the wash water by drum rotation).
b. Less water is needed for both the wash and rinse cycles
c. Drying obviously cannot be done by spinning, but by heating the load inside the cabinet to evaporate excess water

As you see, the requirements are basically the same for both machines, but the results are achieved by different processes and actions of the machine. We will deal later with the similarity of functional parts between these two different types of machine.

What follows is a general description of a typical wash cycle which is not based on any particular model. It is just a simple guide to help you to understand the procedures involved.

With the machine loaded and checked to make sure the spray arms will not be obstructed by utensils or pan handles etc., protruding either above or below their working position, (a gentle tap to spin them will confirm this and they should spin freely), the detergent dispenser filled with a recommended powder and the door firmly closed, select the programme suitable for the degree of soiling on the dishes etc. The machine is now ready to be switched on, which depending on the style of machine may involve a separate switch or simply pulling out the timer selection knob. The machine will then begin to fill with water via the inlet valve until it reaches a preset level and then the heating of the water and washing takes place.

Note – on average, the machine will take in only 9 litres of water per fill, (see *Water level control*). Generally, the water used will have been softened by the machine's own water softening device, but we will go more into that in the chapter on internal water softening and regeneration.

Washing of the dishes is by means of spray arms mounted either above or below the load baskets. Water is pumped to the spray arms under pressure by a large single phase asynchronous induction motor called the wash pump or circulation pump. Most wash pumps have a pump rate of 150 litres per minute. The bottom spray arm is usually mounted directly in line with its outlet and takes approximately two-thirds (100 litres per minute) of this flow rate and the top spray arm is fed the remaining third (50 litres p/m). This arrangement allows the more delicate items to be cleaned in the top basket, while pots and pans with heavier soiling can be cleaned in the lower basket.

Water is fed to both spray arms simultaneously. Each spray arm has a series of angled slots cut or formed in the flat surface of each arm and a hole at each end of the arm on opposing sides. The dynamic force of the water propelled from the slots and holes cause the arms to rotate in a given direction. This rotation then delivers water under pressure with the cleaning agent in suspension, to all areas of the inner cabinet and blasts clean the contents of the machine. A more detailed description of spray arm is found later in the book. Although the means of supplying water to the top spray arms differs between manufacturers, the basic principle remains the same.

The lower section of the machine is shaped so as to cause a sump effect and a reservoir for the wash pump, thus causing a sealed system of continous wash water movement.

Heating of the water is via a submerged element and takes place simultaneously with the wash action. At a preset time or temperature, the detergent powder container is energised to release its contents to the wash liquid. Washing will now continue for the duration of the type of programme selected, i.e. Long – heavy soiling, Short – light soiling etc. At the end of this temperature/timed sequence, the machine will empty out the now dirty water containing the soiling in suspension, after first filtering out any large pieces of debris by means of a cleanable filter situated in the sump recess.

After the time allowed for emptying has elapsed, the timer will move on and initiate a rinse sequence. The machine will fill to correct level, again engaging the wash pump when this level is reached, but this time, without the heater in circuit as only cold rinsing is required. After a timed sequence, the machine will empty out the first rinse water in readiness for the second rinse which unlike the first rinse, is heated. Following a preset time, an additive from the rinse aid compartment is added to the water. (See *Rinse aid dispensers*). On completion of the last hot rinse, the water is pumped away and the latent heat of the dishes etc. will effect quick and uniform drying of the load by steaming off the excess moisture.

Times and temperatures and the number of rinses will vary depending on make and model of your machine, but again the basic principles remain constant.

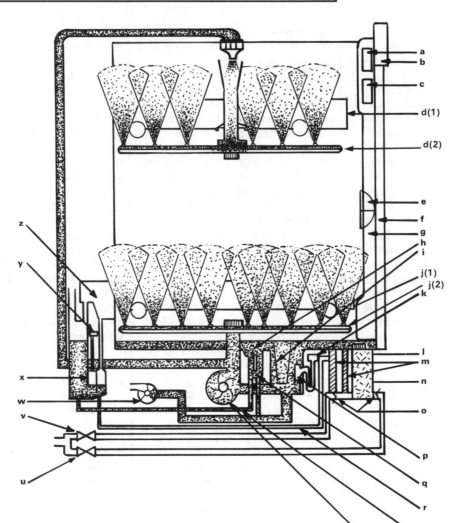

Fig.1
Shown is a theoretical layout of the internal parts of a dishwasher. This layout includes float system, pressure system and venturi level systems. It is not meant to represent your particular machine, but to give some help in identifying parts and the general operation of dishwashers.

A   Programme or timer unit (in this instance, mounted in the door).
B   Door facia and handle.
C   Rinse aid unit.
D   (1) Upper load basket.
D   (2) Upper spray arm (could also be supplied by lower water jet).

E   Door mounted detergent dispenser.
F   Door outer.
G   Door inner.
H   Venturi float system.
I   Large base mounted filter.
J   (1) Bottom load basket.
J   (2) Bottom spray arm (could also supply jet from centre to supply upper arm).
K   Overfill pressure switch.
L   Water softener unit.
M   Sealed resin compartments of softener unit.
N   Refillable salt reservoir.
O   Softener feed non-return valve.
P   Overfill pressure vessel.
Q   Venturi float valve system.

R   Softenend water supply to load compartment or venturi.
S   Venturi hose system (if used on your machine).
T   Main circulation pump chamber.
U   Inlet valve with reduced outlet or regeneration cycle.
V   Main inlet valve for machine (via softener unit in this instance).
W   Outlet pump chamber.
X   Pressure vessel for level system (may also be float on some machines).
Y   Pressure system level switch and hose.
Z   Steam vent and air break unit.

Fig.2
One version of sump moulding fixing

A. Load compartment base.
B. Clamp band or securing bracket.
C. Rubber moulded seal.
D. Moulded plastic sump unit.

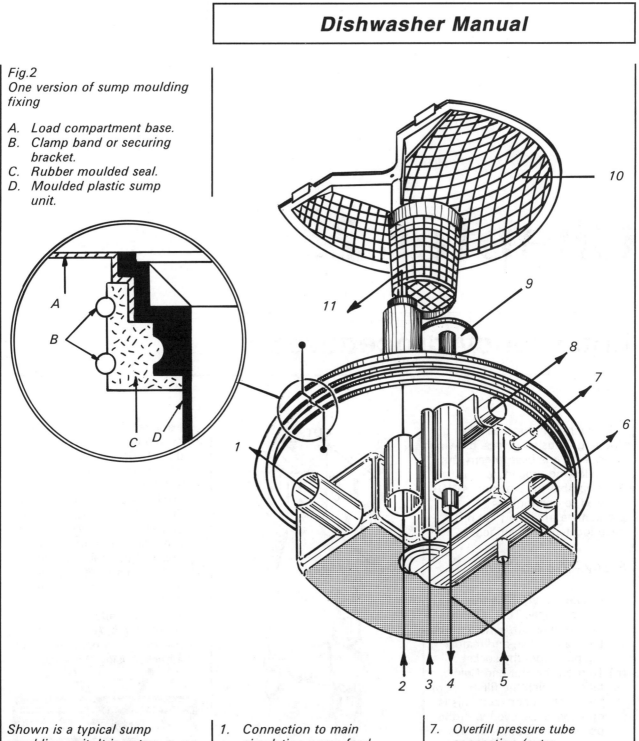

Shown is a typical sump moulding unit. It is not representative of any particular machine but shows the basic requirements of the sump. Some units may incorporate the circulation pump chamber and outlet pump chambers within the unit. Not all have connections for venturi level systems. This unit highlights most, if not all variations and connections.

1. *Connection to main circulation pump feed.*
2. *Supply from the main circulation pump for both upper and lower spray arms.*
3. *Inlet for venturi level valve.*
4. *Outlet for venturi level valve.*
5. *Drain tube connection from venturi level chamber.*
6. *Connection for outlet pump.*
7. *Overfill pressure tube connection (extra internal pressure chamber).*
8. *Supply to upper spray arm. (2 and 8 interconnect).*
9. *Venturi float unit.*
10. *Main sump water filter with both large and fine filter mesh.*
11. *Lower spray arm supply and mounting point.*

Chapter 2.

Emergency procedures

With such symptoms as leaking, flooding, unusual noises, blowing fuses, etc., it is best to carry out the following procedure. It is essential that the machine is NOT allowed to continue its programme until the fault has been located and rectified.

Firstly – Do Not Panic

(a) Isolate the machine from the mains supply. That is, turn the machine off, switch off at the wall socket, and remove the plug from the socket.

(b) Turn off the Hot and Cold taps to which the fill hoses of the machine connect. This is done because, even with the power turned off, if a valve is at fault, it may be jammed in the open position. The machine will still fill, as turning the power or the machine off will make no difference to this type of fault.

(c) At this point, the power and water should be disconnected. Even now, if there is still water in the machine, it could still be leaking. Any water that may still be in the machine can be

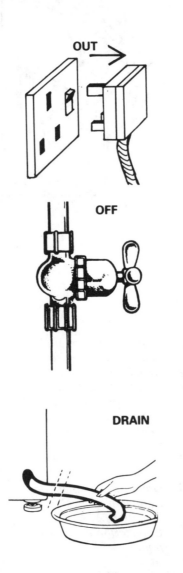

extracted from the machine by syphoning. This is easily done by lifting the outlet hose from its usual position, and lowering it below the level of water in the machine. This will allow the water to drain (unless of course, there is a blockage in the outlet hose!). The easiest method is if the outlet hose will reach to an outside door, where all that is needed is a little movement, and the water should drain. Alternatively, the water can be drained into a bucket using the same

technique. To stop the water, lift the pipe above the height of the machine. Repeat this process until the machine is empty.

(d) Do not open the door until all of the previous steps have been carried out, and a few minutes have elapsed to allow the machine to cool. In cases where the machine was on a very hot wash, wait about half an hour.

When all of these steps have been carried out, and the load has been removed from the cabinet, it is then possible to calmly sit down and start to work out what the problem may be, and form the plan of action in a logical and concise manner.

Chapter 3

A General Safety Guide

Most people have a healthy respect for electricity and understand its potential assets as well as the way it can be dangerous, sometimes lethal, if taken for granted and misused.

Electricity at all voltages is to be respected. Those that do not observe the basic rules of electricity are not only a danger to themselves but to those around them. Electrical accidents should be regarded as avoidable. Most are due to plain carelessness and the failure to follow basic rules of electricity even when they are already known.

There are in the region of sixteen million homes in Britain supplied with electricity, each home having on average twenty-five electrical appliances. With such a volume of items, it may be a surprise to find that fatalities due to electrical accidents are less than eighty per year. Although this is a small percentage figure in terms of population and only represents 1 per cent of the 8000 deaths resulting from accidents in the home, the figure is still too high.

The three most common causes of shock or fires from electrical appliances are:

1. Faulty wiring of the appliances, ie frayed or damaged flex or cable, incorrect fuse, poor socket, poor/damaged plug, incorrectly wired plug, etc.
2. Misuse of the appliance; for example, a hairdryer or similar electrical appliance being used in the bathroom, or an electrical power tool being used outside in the rain or in the wet. The rules relating to electrical items in bathrooms are strict for good reason. The combination of water and electricity greatly increases the possibility of injury.
3. Continuing to use an electrical appliance knowing it to be unsafe, for example with a cracked casing, faulty plug, damaged cable, faulty on/off switch, etc.

By having the awareness of the need for safety, several of the above faults are avoidable. Others can be eliminated by regular inspection and immediate correction of faults, failure or wear. As for misuse, this may be due to a purely foolhardy approach or genuine ignorance of danger. This can be overcome by understanding and, above all, acting upon the guidelines in this book. If at anytime you feel you lack the ability to do a particular job yourself, then it is best not to try. You can still carry out the diagnosis of the problem thus ensuring that any work carried out by a repair company is correct. This alone can sometimes save much time and expense.

DO'S
• Thoroughly read all the information in this book prior to putting it into practice.
• Isolate any appliance before repair or inspection commences.
• Correctly fit the mains plug (see: *Plugs and Sockets*), ensuring the connections are in the correct position, tight and the cord clamp is fitted on the outer insulation of the cable.
• Check that the socket used is in good condition and has a sound earth path (see: *Basics – Electrical*).
• Take time to consider the problem at hand and allow enough time to complete the job without rushing.
• Follow a methodical approach to the stripdown of the item and make notes. This helps greatly with reassembly.

- Double-check everything.
- Ask or seek help if in doubt.
- Ensure that a Residual Current Device (RCD) is in circuit when using electrical equipment outdoors.

DON'TS

- Do not work on any machine that is still plugged in even if the socket switch is **OFF**. Always isolate fully – **PLUG OUT**.
- Do not allow portable mains appliances to be used in bathrooms or shower rooms from a socket outside the room. It may seem harmless to run an extension lead from a convenient socket on the landing so that a portable fan heater or hairdryer can be used in the bathroom, but it is extremely dangerous and MUST NOT be done under any circumstances.
- Do not use mains-powered equipment outdoors in rain or damp conditions.
- Do not in **ANY** circumstances repair damaged flex or cables with insulation tape.
- Do not sacrifice safety by affecting a temporary repair.

GENERAL

Consider your own safety and that of other people.
Act in a way that prevents incidents from becoming accidents.
Use your common sense and think before acting.
Tidy workplaces make safer workplaces.
Identify hazards.
Observe the rule of Safety First.
Never underestimate the dangers.
Switch off! Always withdraw plug and disconnect from mains.
Appliances vary – make sure you have a suitable replacement part.
For screws use a screwdriver, for nuts a spanner, for knurled nuts use pliers.

Examine and clean all connections before fitting new parts.
Tighten firmly all screws and nuts.
Your safety depends on these simple rules.

Fuses: Up to 250 watts 1 amp; 750 watts 3 amp; 750 to 3000 watts 13 amp.
Insulation is for your protection. Don't interfere.
Renew worn or damaged appliance flex.
Secure flex clamps and all protective covers.
Test physically and electrically on completion.

Plug wiring

Plug wiring must be connected according to the following code to ensure safety. The colours are as follows:

Live – Brown (or Red), symbol 'L'
Neutral – Blue (or Black), symbol 'N'
Earth – Green/Yellow (or Green), symbol 'E'

The colours in brackets are those used until the newer and current international standards were introduced. They may still be found on some equipment. Plug terminals are identified either by colour (old or new) or by the letter symbols shown.

Physical safety

Great care must be exercised when removing or handling the panels of any dishwasher. The edges of formed metal parts are rarely cleanly finished after pressing or moulding during manufacture. Generally only the edges that the user would normally come into contact with are deburred and finished. Edges exposed during a repair can be extremely sharp especially on formed stainless steel panels and seam welded joints on the outer of the load compartment. Take care not to slip when servicing or removing components within these areas and avoid running fingers along or near exposed panel edges.

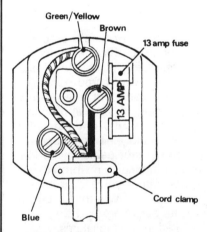

Ensure that only the correct rated fuse is used. It is dangerous to exceed the required rating. Even if the appliance appears to work normally little or no protection will be afforded should a fault occur.

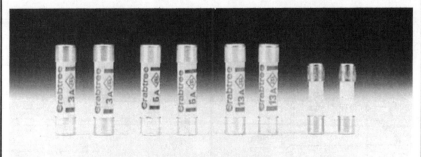

Chapter 4

Special note: Variations in supply systems used in countries other than the U.K.
As detailed in the text in this chapter, various types of earthing systems may be encountered – one of the most popular being the P.M.E. system whereby neutral and earth are BONDED (linked) at the supply point to the property. The choice of which supply system (and ultimately which earth system your property has) is a matter for your supply authority. The requirement of a sound earth path however is common to all domestic systems.

Basics – electrical

For the sake of safety around the home or office, a basic understanding of electricity is essential. Even if you don't intend to carry out any repairs or servicing of your appliance yourself, a sound understanding of household electrical supply will prove invaluable in the long run. Ignorance is no protection against either yours or a third party's errors, whether it be on repairs, servicing or the installation of appliances. It is with this in mind that this chapter has been written. It is not an in-depth study of the subject – there are many books that contain more detailed information for those who want to know more about electricity.

In this instance, the aim is to impart a safe knowledge without too much technical data. Some may argue that a little knowledge is a dangerous thing, but I believe that total ignorance is a much greater danger. To be informed is to be enlightened – to be aware of danger helps one to avoid it and to understand how and why certain safety criteria should be adopted.

Figure 1 shows a simplified, but typical household supply. The substation has power supplied to it at very high voltage (400,000 volts) in three-phase form. This supply is converted at the substation, via a transformer, down to 240 volt

single-phase and is then distributed to our homes. In normal circumstances, current flows from the live supply of the substation's transformer, through the electrical items being used in the house and back via the neutral conductor (cable) to the substation transformer's neutral pole (a closed loop). The neutral terminal of the transformer is in turn connected to the ground (earth – meaning in this case,

Fig. 1 Typical household supply.

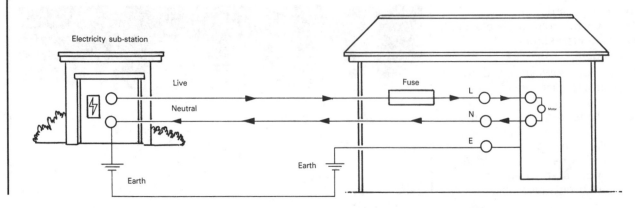

Electricity sub-station

Live

Neutral

Earth

Fuse

L

N

E

Motor

Earth

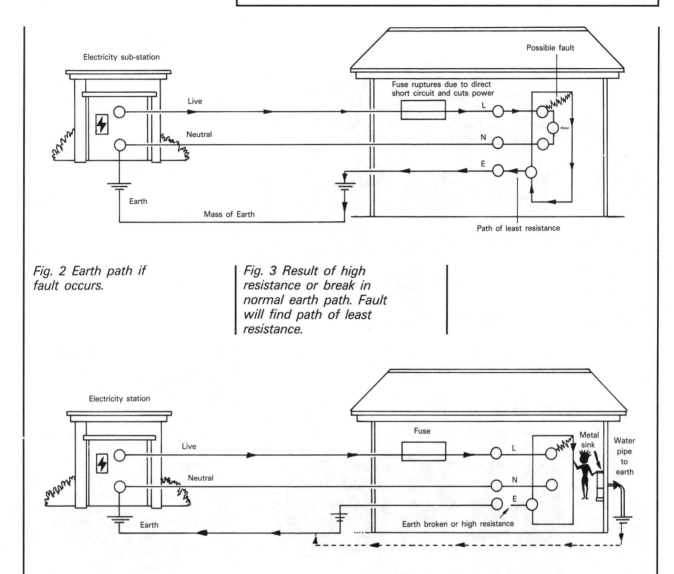

Fig. 2 Earth path if fault occurs.

Fig. 3 Result of high resistance or break in normal earth path. Fault will find path of least resistance.

the general mass of the earth), as shown in Figure 2. It is usual to use the armoured sheath of the electricity supply authority's cable in order to provide a low impedance continuous link back to the supply transformers' star point. Various types of earthing can be encountered: connection to the armoured sheath of the authority's supply cable; own earth rod; transformer earth rod via general mass of the earth; or the increasingly popular neutral conductor of the authority's supply cable (often called PME – protective multiple earthing or TN-C-S system).

The earth loop path is designed to encourage current to flow, in the event of an earth fault, to enable the protective devices within the consumer unit (fuse, MCB or RCD) to operate in order to isolate the supply to the circuit. Failure to cause the protective device to operate will result in the appliance remaining live with the consequence that any person touching the appliance will receive a nasty, possibly fatal, electric shock. Remember, electricity always takes the route of least resistance, therefore a person standing on the ground touching a live appliance can provide a low

resistance alternative earth path resulting in a severe shock or worse. For this reason, the resistance of the earth loop path must be low enough to allow sufficient fault current to flow to operate the protective fuse or circuit breaker.

The term used for testing earthing performance is earth loop impedance, which means checking to see if the current flow is impeded and if it is, by how much. This test requires a specialised meter giving resistance figures in ohms, the maximum reading recommended by the IEE (Institution of Electrical Engineers) being 1.1 ohms for a domestic earth path, unless a

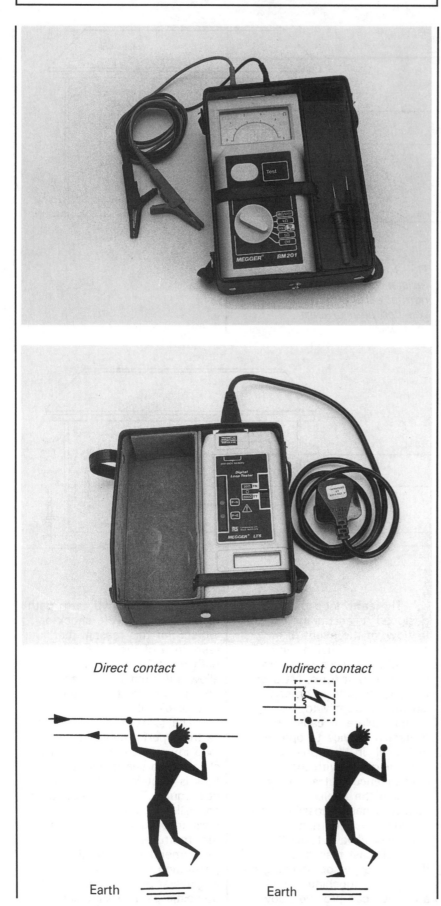

A versatile test meter incorporating 500v insulation test facility.

Direct contact

Indirect contact

Earth

Earth

A professional earth loop test meter gives the only true indication of the earth path quality.

Type 1 MCB is in circuit in which case a 2 ohm maximum is permissible.

Note: A correct test cannot be carried out using a low voltage meter because a fault can exist that allows the low voltage of, say, 9 volts to pass easily (eg just one tiny strand of wire poorly connected) but would break down and go high-resistance or open-circuit if a working voltage of 240 v at 13 amps was applied. Though low voltage testing will give an indication of earth path, it cannot indicate quality. The earth loop impedance meter gives a clearer indication of earth quality in more realistic conditions.

What is an earth fault?

An earth fault is defined as the condition where electricity flows to earth when in normal circumstances, it should not do so. There are two recognised ways in which this may happen: direct and indirect. *Direct.* When contact is made directly with the current-carrying conductor which is designed to carry that current. *Indirect.* Touching a part of an appliance, that would not normally carry current but is doing so due to a fault.

What is a consumer unit?

The consumer unit is where the supply into the house is split into separate circuits, ie those for lights, sockets etc. It houses

A typical house installation.

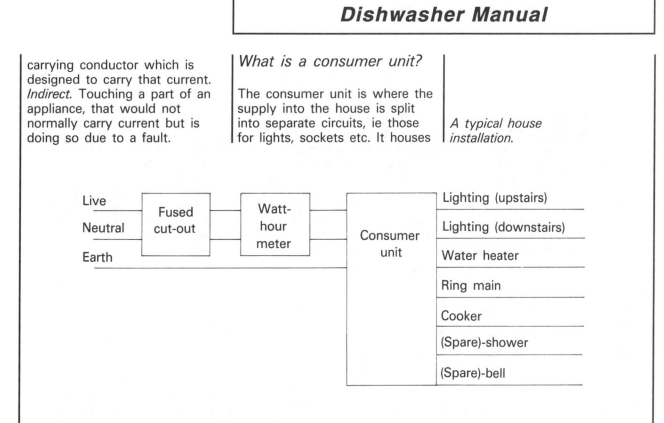

Live		Lighting (upstairs)
Neutral	Fused cut-out → Watt-hour meter → Consumer unit	Lighting (downstairs)
Earth		Water heater
		Ring main
		Cooker
		(Spare)-shower
		(Spare)-bell

Modern consumer unit with RCD main switch and MCBs on all circuits.

a main isolation switch or combined RCD which is used to isolate (remove power from) all the circuits in the house. Also housed within the unit are various fuse-carriers for cartridge or rewirable fuses or a Miniature Circuit Breaker (MCB) in place of fuses. Each circuit leading from the consumer unit has its own rating of fuse or MCB and only that fuse rating and no other must be used.

Typical older-style consumer unit with isolation switch and wired fuses only.

Note: Even when the consumer unit is switched off there is still a live supply to it. Do not remove the covers of the consumer unit or tackle any inspection or repair to this item without seeking further information. Faults other than fuse renewal are best left to skilled electrical engineers. Although assistance may be available from other publications, extreme care should be exercised. As mentioned earlier, it is not the aim of this book to invite the repair or maintenance of items that are not fully isolated.

All about fuses

As mentioned earlier, two versions of fuses are to be found: the cartridge type and the rewirable type. The rewirable type is difficult and fiddly to rewire and the cartridge type, although easier to renew, is often difficult to obtain. Both these systems have drawbacks in being awkward and not very 'user friendly'.

An ordinary fuse is simply a weak link designed to break at a preset rating. If a circuit is overloaded or a short circuit occurs, the resulting overload will cause the fuse to melt and sever the supply. Unless a direct short circuit occurs, however, the overload on the fuse may not be enough to cause the fuse to blow because it has a fair degree of leeway over its rating value. It, therefore, offers only basic safety and will not afford any personal safety as the time taken to break is usually too long.

Mechanism of miniature circuit breaker.
A.   Arc runner
B.   Arc chamber
C.   Fixed contact
D.   Moving contact
E1. Solenoid coil
E2. Moving core
F.   Trip bar
G.   Thermo-metal
H1. Wiring terminal
H2. Wiring terminal
I.   Fixing

To the old familiar imperial ratings for fuses and circuit breakers have now been added the international Renard ratings. A complete changeover will eventually be effected for common market standardization.

Fuse manufacturers are still using the imperial sizes whilst circuit breaker manufacturers have mostly changed to the new ratings. An equivalence chart is shown below:

Current Rating

Imp.	Renard	Typical Circuit
5	6	Lighting
10	10	
15	16	I mm. htr
20	20	
30	32	Ring main
45	40	Cooker/ shower

Miniature Circuit Breakers

The miniature circuit breaker (MCB) is now widely used and overcomes all the problems associated with ordinary fuses. The MCB is a small sophisticated unit that affords a much higher degree of protection than an ordinary fuse. It is tamper-proof and the unit involved is easily identified when one has tripped (switch moves to 'OFF' position). Most importantly, MCBs cannot be reset if the fault still exists which eliminates the practice of putting in the wrong fuse wire or cartridge to get things working – a foolish and most dangerous practice! MCBs are available in similar ratings to ordinary fuses and operate in two ways. Referring to the accompanying photograph, current flows into the unit at 'H1' and along 'G' through coil 'E1' and on to the moving contact 'D' (shown here open circuit). Contact 'D' in the ON position would be resting on fixed contact 'C' and so current would flow to H2.

Two fault conditions may arise; firstly, short circuit. This type of fault would quickly increase the current flow through the unit. Section E1, being a coil would increase its magnetic field and as a result attract E2 into the coil centre. This action trips the mechanism arm 'F' and causes 'C - D' to open circuit. Conductor 'A' and arc chamber 'B' act to suppress the arc formed on the contact point. This is done by the arc runners drawing the arc across the arc chamber where it is chopped into small arcs which are quickly extinguished. The action of an MCB is much quicker than an ordinary fuse wire. The second type of fault could simply be an overload on the circuit and, although exceeding the safe working load of the circuit, it would not cause the solenoid to trip. In this type of situation, the current flowing through 'G' causes the conductor to heat up. The conductor is made of a tri-metal plate that bends when heated. The bending action of the conductor trips arm 'F', causing 'C' and 'D' to open circuit as before. This operation again is much better than fuse wire and calibration to higher tolerances is possible.

Note: These units are

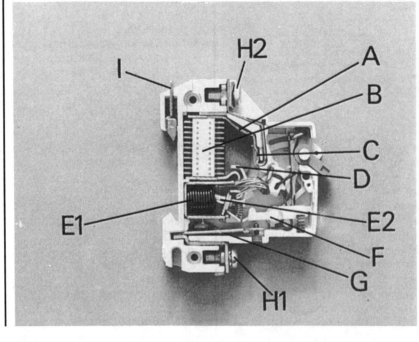

factory-calibrated to extremely accurate tolerances and must not be tampered with nor attempts made to readjust them. The internal workings are only shown to help understand their operation. In the event of faults or failures, a new replacement unit must be fitted. No repair or adjustment is possible.

Unfortunately, neither fuses nor miniature circuit breakers alone can give protection to anyone involved in a DIRECT EARTH situation. Indeed, the same can apply in the case of an INDIRECT EARTH contact. This may sound confusing, but it should be realised that in a 'direct contact' situation a person is literally shorting out Live and Earth, whereas in an indirect contact situation, the Live to Earth path is already there because the equipment itself is connected to earth. The reason the fuse hasn't blown or the circuit breaker tripped is because the fault is not great enough to operate the safety mechanism, yet is great enough to be fatal. For instance, a 10 amp fuse would never blow with an 8 amp earth fault on the circuit, yet 8 amps constitutes a very dangerous level of earth fault current.

Residual Current Devices

To afford a higher degree of protection, another device has been developed, available in various forms.
1. Mounted within the consumer unit to protect all or selected circuits.
2. As individual socket protection.
3. An adaptor to be used as portable protection and used where required.

The name given to this device in all its forms is the Residual Current Device (RCD). It may also be called a Residual Current Circuit Breaker (RCCB). In the early days of its introduction, it was known as an Earth Leakage Circuit Breaker (ELCB).

The primary protection is the integrity of the earthing, RCDs, in addition to the earthing, provide a much higher degree of protection depending upon the degree of sensitivity. For personal protection it is recommended that a sensitivity of 30 mA is used.

It is generally considered that an earth fault of 1A or more is a fire risk, 50 mA or more provides a shock risk which can have varying effects upon the human body depending upon the value of earth fault current and the body resistance of the person and, of course, their state of health. The heartbeat cycle is about 0.75 second. It is therefore necessary to cut off the fault current in less than one cardiac cycle. The Wiring Regulations stipulate that for Indirect Contact protection isolation must occur within 0.4 second.

How does an RCD work?

An RCD protects by constantly monitoring the current flowing in the live and neutral wires supplying a circuit or an individual item of equipment. In normal circumstances the current flowing in the two wires is equal but, when an earth leakage occurs due to a fault or an accident, an imbalance occurs and this is detected by the RCD which

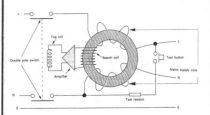

automatically cuts off the power in a split second.

To be effective, the RCD must operate very quickly and at a low earth fault current. Those most frequently recommended are designed to detect earth leakage faults in excess of 30 mA (30/1000 of an amp) and to disconnect the power supply within 200 ms (the rated sensitivity); these limits are well inside the safety margin within which electrocution or fire would not be expected to occur.

It should now be apparent that RCDs are designed to sever mains current should your electrical appliance malfunction electrically, or should you cut through the mains cable of your lawnmower for instance. They are simply a failsafe device and should be used as such. In our opinion, used correctly they are an invaluable asset to your household.

NOTE: The use of an RCD must be in addition to normal overload protection, ie fuses or MCBs, and not instead of it. All residual current devices have a test button facility. It is essential that this is tested regularly to verify that the device operates. For use with adaptors or sockets, or for outside use, test before each operation. If failure occurs (does not trip, or trip appears sluggish or hard to obtain) have the unit tested immediately. This will require an RCD test meter and is best left to a qualified electrician.

The RCD units shown were kindly provided by Crabtree Electrical Industries Ltd, Walsall, West Midlands. All the units manufactured by them are made to the highest possible standards.

A simplified RCD circuit.

Chapter 5

Tools and equipment

Modern dish washing machines do not require very specialised tools. Many of the routine repairs such as blocked pumps, renewal of door seals and hoses can normally be completed with a selection of the following tools. Crossblade and flatblade screwdrivers, combination pliers, simple multimeter, pliers.

Most people who are D.I.Y. orientated will own one or more of these items already. A useful addition to this selection would be a 'Mole' wrench, a socket and/or box spanner set, soft-face hammer and circlip pliers. These would help with the larger jobs, such as motor removal and motor bearing removal.

Bearing removal/renewal and the like may also require such things as bearing pullers. As these can be expensive to buy, it is best to hire them from a tool hire specialist for the short period that you require them. Local garages may also be willing to let you hire them for a small fee.

It will not prove difficult to build up a selection of tools capable of tackling the faults that you are likely to find on your machine. Most of the large D.I.Y. stores will stock most of the tools that you require, often at a good saving.

When buying tools check the quality, as a cheap spanner or socket set is only a waste of money if it bends, or snaps in your hand the moment you get it home! Having said that, there are many tools on the market that are of a reasonable quality and are inexpensive – try to buy the best that your budget will allow. Remember – the tools that you buy are a long term investment and should give you years of useful service.

As with any investment, it is wise to look after it and tools should be treated the same. Having spent time and money on tools, they should be kept in a clean and serviceable condition. Ensure that they are clean and dry before storage.

Chapter 6

Basics – plumbing

Although the machine may have been working correctly in its present position for some time, the incorrect installation of a machine may cause faults many months later. Because of this time span, the faults are not associated with bad plumbing and can cause the D.I.Y. engineer to look for other faults, which is very time consuming and annoying. Having said this, it is therefore worth a few minutes examining the existing pipework, and checking the manufacturer's installation details. These details will be found in the manufacturer's booklet that came with the machine. Even if the installation of your machine was left to an "Expert", it is still advisable to read this section, as the chances are that they will not have read the installation details either!

For those of you who cannot find the manufacturer's booklet, what follows is a brief description of plumbing requirements that apply to nearly all automatic dishwashers and washing machines, and the reasons that they should be adhered to.

If the machine is to be plumbed in "Hot and Cold", then isolation taps must be fitted. (If your dishwasher has only one inlet hose connection, it is advisable to plumb the machine to the cold supply only.) This enables the water supply to be cut off between the normal house supply and that of the washer.

Note: The rubber hoses connected to these taps should be positioned so that they don't get trapped when the machine is pushed back, or rub against any rough surfaces during the machines operation. Both of these conditons can cause the hose to wear, due to the slight movement of the hose when the valves open and close. Also

ensure that no loops have been formed in the hot supply hose (if fitted). In the beginning this will not cause any trouble, but as the hose gets older and the hot water takes effect, the hose will soften and a kink will form. This will then cause a restriction or complete stoppage of water to the machine. This can also happen to the cold hose, although it is very rare, due to the increased pressure in the cold system.

Diagram A – Correct plumbing.

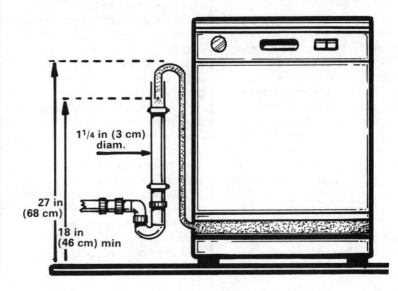

1¼ in (3 cm) diam.

27 in (68 cm)

18 in (46 cm) min

The next thing to do, is check that there is adequate water pressure to operate. First select a normal wash cycle and switch on. The machine should fill to working level within FOUR minutes. The same should apply when a rinse cycle has been selected. This gives a rough indication that the water pressure is adequate to open and close the valves. This is because the valves are pressure operated and a 4 p.s.i. minimum is required for their correct operation. The cold pressure is usually governed by the outside mains pressure, but the hot water pressure is governed by the height of the hot water tank or its header tank.

Problems can arise when the tanks are less than eight feet higher than the water valve they are supplying. This is often found in bungalows and some flats. If a slow fill is suspected, check the small filter that can be found inside all valves, when the inlet hose is unscrewed. These can be removed and cleaned by simply pulling them out gently with pliers. Care must be taken not to damage the filter or allow any small particles to get passed when you remove it. Clean water is normally supplied to the valves, but in many cases old pipework or the limescale deposits from boilers, etc. can collect at these points.

Outlet hose

The outlet hose MUST fit into a pipe larger than itself, thus giving an 'Air Brake' to eliminate syphoning. The height of the outlet hose is also important if syphoning is to be avoided. Syphoning can occur when the end of the outlet hose is below the level of water in the machine. This would give rise to the fault of the machine emptying at the same time as filling, and if the machine were to be turned off, would continue to empty the water from the machine, down to its syphon level.

Kinks and loops can also

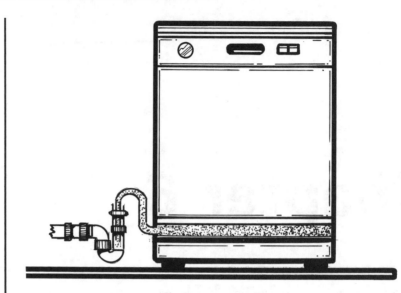

Diagram B – Incorrect plumbing, causing syphoning.

Note: Height of outlet hose. Syphoning will take place due to the outlet hose being too low or too far down drain tube.

affect the outlet pipe, and cause several problems to the wash, rinse and dry programmes.

Self plumbing in

When a machine is to be fitted in close proximity to an existing sink unit, you can take advantage of the new style *'SELFBORE'* taps and outlet systems now available. These simple and effective D.I.Y. fittings will save both time and money.

In most cases, the fitting of these taps can be done with only a screwdriver and no soldering is required. You do not even need to drain or turn off the main water system at all.

At this stage, I feel it is better to give you some visual help rather than pages of text. The following pages show you how easy the fitting of such units can be!

Self plumbing out

1. Select the most convenient place in the waste pipe 1^1/$_4$" (31mm) or 1^1/$_2$" (38mm) dia.
2. Disconnect components (as shown above). Place saddle halves around waste pipe, removing saddle inserts if pipe is 1½" dia. Ensure that the 'O' ring is seated in recess. Tighten screws by stages to give an even and maximum pressure on waste pipe.
3. Insert cutting tool and screw home (clockwise) until hole is cut in waste pipe. Repeat to ensure a clean entry.
4. Remove cutter and screw in elbow. Use locking nut ⑤ to determine final position of elbow and tighten, or screw non-return valve ⑥ directly into saddle piece.
5. To complete installation, choose correct size hose coupling to suit drain hose and secure hose with hose clip (not included in kit).
* It is important to regularly remove and clean deposits from non-return valve. Simply unscrew retaining collar ④

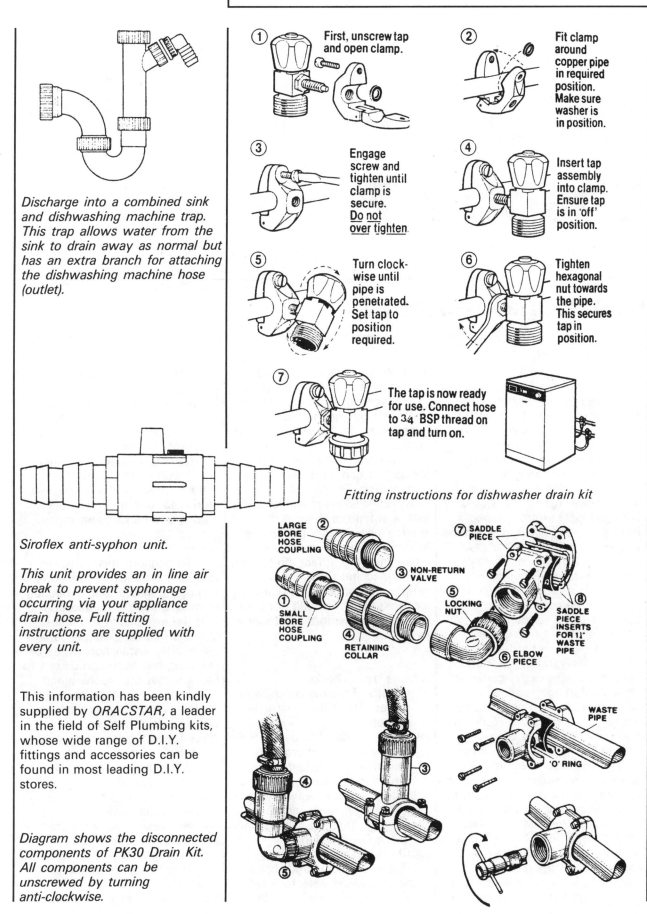

Discharge into a combined sink and dishwashing machine trap. This trap allows water from the sink to drain away as normal but has an extra branch for attaching the dishwashing machine hose (outlet).

① First, unscrew tap and open clamp.

② Fit clamp around copper pipe in required position. Make sure washer is in position.

③ Engage screw and tighten until clamp is secure. Do not over tighten.

④ Insert tap assembly into clamp. Ensure tap is in 'off' position.

⑤ Turn clockwise until pipe is penetrated. Set tap to position required.

⑥ Tighten hexagonal nut towards the pipe. This secures tap in position.

⑦ The tap is now ready for use. Connect hose to ¾" BSP thread on tap and turn on.

Fitting instructions for dishwasher drain kit

Siroflex anti-syphon unit.

This unit provides an in line air break to prevent syphonage occurring via your appliance drain hose. Full fitting instructions are supplied with every unit.

① SMALL BORE HOSE COUPLING
② LARGE BORE HOSE COUPLING
③ NON-RETURN VALVE
④ RETAINING COLLAR
⑤ LOCKING NUT
⑥ ELBOW PIECE
⑦ SADDLE PIECE
⑧ SADDLE PIECE INSERTS FOR 1¼" WASTE PIPE

This information has been kindly supplied by ORACSTAR, a leader in the field of Self Plumbing kits, whose wide range of D.I.Y. fittings and accessories can be found in most leading D.I.Y. stores.

WASTE PIPE

'O' RING

Diagram shows the disconnected components of PK30 Drain Kit. All components can be unscrewed by turning anti-clockwise.

Chapter 7

Functional testing

Whenever possible the symptoms of the fault should be confirmed by the operation of the machine up to the point of the suspected fault, whereupon the machine should be stopped, disconnected from the mains supply and the relevant flowchart followed. For major leaks, blown fuses, etc., this is NOT practical (more damage may result by repeated operation of the machine). In these cases, the fault is known and further confirmation would be of little benefit. This may in fact, result in further damage to the machine or its surroundings.

Being able to assess and locate a fault may at first seem a difficult thing to do, but if a few simple procedures are carried out prior to starting the work, they will help cut down on the time spent on the machine. Hopping in a random fashion from one part of the machine to another, hoping that you will come across the fault and subsequently repair it, is hardly the best approach to repair work. This is not the way to tackle any job. Without doubt, the best method of fault finding is to be gained from your own experience of the machine, the fault with it and its location and rectification based on all the available information. Always remember a methodical approach to the work in hand, saves time and effort by eliminating unnecessary replacements based on guesswork.

However there are a few things that can be done before such testing. These will ascertain if, in fact, it is the machine itself that is at fault or if an external/user fault is the source. Indeed, a large percentage of repair calls, are in fact, not a fault of the machine at all. Before jumping to conclusions, pause for a moment. You will not only save time and effort, but money as well.

A few simple checks.
(a) Check – That the machine is turned ON at the electricity socket.
(b) Check – That the fuse in the plug is intact and working. This can be checked by replacing the suspected fuse with one out of a working item of the same rating.
(c) Check – That the tap/taps are in the ON position.
(d) Check – That the door is closed correctly, and that a wash cycle is selected and the knob or switch has been pulled/pushed to the ON position.
(e) Check – That the machine is not on a 'Rinse and (pre-rinse) hold' position. This on most machines will cause the machine to stand idle until instructed to do otherwise.
If the fault still remains, the next step is to determine its true nature, and subsequent repair.

Throughout this book, reference is made to functional testing to ensure that the action of the machine is correct and that the installation is suitable. Use the following sequence as a guide after installation, repair or servicing has been carried out to confirm that the machine and installation is working correctly. By following the sequence, you will be able to test where practical, all the functions of the machine and its plumbing installation in a safe and efficient manner. Although slight modifications may be necessary to suit model variations, the test will suit most if not all makes of machines that use mechanical timers/programmers.

Note: Prior to functional testing, make sure that the machine is as near to level as possible, ideally this should be within 2 degrees of horizontal. All machines have adjustable feet for this purpose.

A typical dishwasher installation and functional test routine

1. Check that the door fits smoothly into the load compartment aperture and latches easily and securely. (On uneven floors, further levelling adjustment may be necessary to compromise between a level position and ease of door closing).
2. Turn on water and electrical supplies to the machine.
3. With the door of the machine down, manually open and close the detergent dispenser several times to verify free movement of the latch mechanism. Ensure that the detergent compartment is clean and free from old detergent residue. Clean thoroughly if required.
   Note: Types of dispenser differ between manufacturers and also the quantity of powder/liquid detergent that they hold. **It is not necessary to use detergent or fill load compartment with crockery for functional testing.**
4. Check that the Rinse Aid dispenser is not empty and make sure that the dosage setting is correct – see chapters on *Rinse aid dispensers* and *Common causes of poor washing results*.

5. Check the salt container level indicator is showing that there is sufficient salt in the reservoir (if fitted). See chapter on *Internal water softeners*. Ensure that adjustment is set to correct hardness of water supply.
6. Close the door securely and select the rinse and hold sequence and switch to the 'on' position. Reference to your particular machine's handbook may be required to obtain the correct setting.
(a) Fill time should be within 4 minutes.
(b) When the wash action starts, i.e. main circulation pump, check for visible leaks from door seal, base, etc. If there is any leakage, end the test sequence and isolate the machine before tracing the problem. See Chapter 11, *Determining the fault*.
(c) During the cycle (averaging between 8 and 12 minutes), listen for water circulating through the spray arms.
(d) Before the cycle has finished, switch off and wait a few seconds to allow the spray arms to come to rest. Open the door and check the level of water within the machine **and** the position of the spray arms. Close the door securely and switch on for 10–15 seconds. Turn off, pause then open the door and check that the arms have come to rest in a different position, thus indicating free rotation. **Note:** opening the door too quickly

will result in water spraying out since the arms will not come to rest the instant the machine is turned off.
(e) Close the door again, switch the machine on and allow the remainder of the rinse and hold cycle to continue.
7. Allow the machine to impulse normally to the empty/drain position.
(a) Visually check the outlet hose stand pipe to verify that the drain is capable of taking all the water being discharged by the machine, i.e. not overflowing from the top of the stand pipe. Blockages in stand pipe drains are not uncommon but they are not a fault of the machine, see Chapter 6 *Basics – plumbing*.
(b) At this point, unlatch the door and only partially lower it in order to check the door safety switch – all functions should cease.
   Note: Opening the door too quickly will result in water spraying out since the arms will not come to rest the instant the machine is turned off.
(c) Close the door and allow the machine to impulse to the stop position.
8. Turn the machine off, open the door and confirm that the emptying cycle did in fact drain the machine correctly. If the machine fails to empty correctly, refer to Chapter 11 – *Determining the fault*.

Chapter 8

General care and attention

For many repairs it is best that the machine be laid on its back or side. Because of the need for as large a load compartment as possible, most of the functional parts of a dishwasher are mounted below the load compartment floor and are easily accessible.

Always ensure that the outer shell of the machine is protected with a suitable cover when attempting to lay the machine down. The machine should be lowered slowly, and when doing this it is a good idea to place a strip of wood under the edge of the machine, to provide room for the fingers for lifting the machine back into its correct position after the repair.

When laying the machine over, care should be taken to protect oneself from injury. Firstly, ensure that the machine is completely disconnected from the main supply, and that the inlet and outlet hoses are removed. Secondly, before attempting to lay the machine over, decide if you need any help. These machines are heavy and a little help may prevent a slipped disc! Thirdly, before attempting to move the machine, ENSURE THAT THE FLOOR IS DRY. A wet floor has no grip, especially if any of the water on it is soapy.

The correct rating of fuse must be used as per the manufacturer's instructions.

The author would like to point out at this time, that any references to manufacturer's names or model numbers, etc., that are used throughout this manual are for the readers' information, and reference purposes only. Whilst every precaution has been taken to ensure that all information is accurate in every detail, the author cannot accept any responsibility for any errors or omissions appertaining to this manual, and shall not be responsible for any damage or injury caused whilst using this manual.

Regular inspection points

A regular internal inspection of your dishwasher may enable you to identify a part that may not be running properly, or find a perished hose before a leak occurs. It is recommended that the following points be checked regularly.
Note: As many of the hoses within a dishwasher carry water under pressure, it is essential that all such hoses and clips are in ''A1'' condition. If in doubt, renew any suspect hose or clip to avoid future major leaks.

Inspect	When	Special notes
Main filter	Weekly – as per manufacturer's manual. Often dependent on usage	Remove and clean thoroughly both small and large particle filter. Rinse thoroughly.
Spray arms	Weekly – as per manufacturer's manual. Often dependent on usage	Remove blockages from slots on the spray arms and check for free rotation.
Rinse aid dispenser	Weekly – as per manufacturer's manual. Often dependent on usage	Check level/content of rinse aid tank. Top up as required.
Salt container	Weekly – as per manufacturer's manual. Often dependent on usage	Check level/content of container. Top up as required.
Valve filters (hot and cold)	6 months	If dirty, pull out with pliers and wash out.
Door seals	6 months	If seal is tacky to the touch, it may be in need of renewal. Clean and remove all food and fat deposits, etc.
All hoses	6 months	As above. Ensure that all corrugations in all hoses are checked thoroughly.
Pump and sump hoses	6 months	Check for any items that may have collected in or at these points. Remove as necessary.
Level machine	Yearly	Check that the machine is standing firmly on the floor and does not rock. Adjust by unscrewing the adjustable feet or packing under the wheels.
Check plug and connectors	After every repair	After repair, look for poor connections in the plug socket. Also look for any cracks or other damage. Renew as necessary.
Taps and washers	After every repair	Check taps for free movement, corrosion and/or leaks.

Chapter 9

Using a flowchart

Flowcharts are used throughout the book, and are designed to help you quickly locate the area or areas of trouble, and to show that a step-by-step approach to even the most difficult of faults, is by far the best way to ensure they are found and rectified easily.

The use of flowcharts to those with some experience of home computers will need little explanation. To those of you who will be seeing them for the first time, here is how they work.

How flowcharts work

To the uninitiated, the use of flowcharts may seem a difficult way of fault finding. This is not the case, and will be quite simple if a few small, but important points are remembered. As you will see in the examples, there are only three main types of symbols used. A rectangular box, a diamond and an elipse. With a little practise, you will become aware how invaluable this method can be in all areas of D.I.Y. work. The construction of one's own flowchart before attempting the job in hand, will be of help when the time comes to reverse the stripdown procedure, i.e., notes can be

made next to the relevant boxes on the flowchart, of what was encountered at that point, i.e., number of screws, positions of wires, etc. Small points – but so vital, and so often forgotten with an unplanned approach.

The rectangular box

This is a process, i.e., in the box is an instruction. Carry it out and rejoin the flowchart where you left it, travelling in the direction indicated by the arrows.

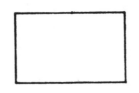

The diamond

This asks a question, i.e., if the answer to the question in the diamond is "yes", then follow the line from the point of the box, i.e., the box asks if a pipe is blocked. The junction to the left is marked *"no"* and the junction to the right is marked *"yes"*. If the pipe is blocked, follow the line to the right.

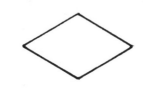

The elipse

This is a terminator. When this box is encountered, you either start a new chart or finish one. The text in the box will indicate the action.

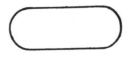

The following example flowchart illustrates the steps involved in carrying out the simple task of opening a closed door, and closing an open door. The arrows indicate the direction to the next step, so as to guide you through the logical sequence.

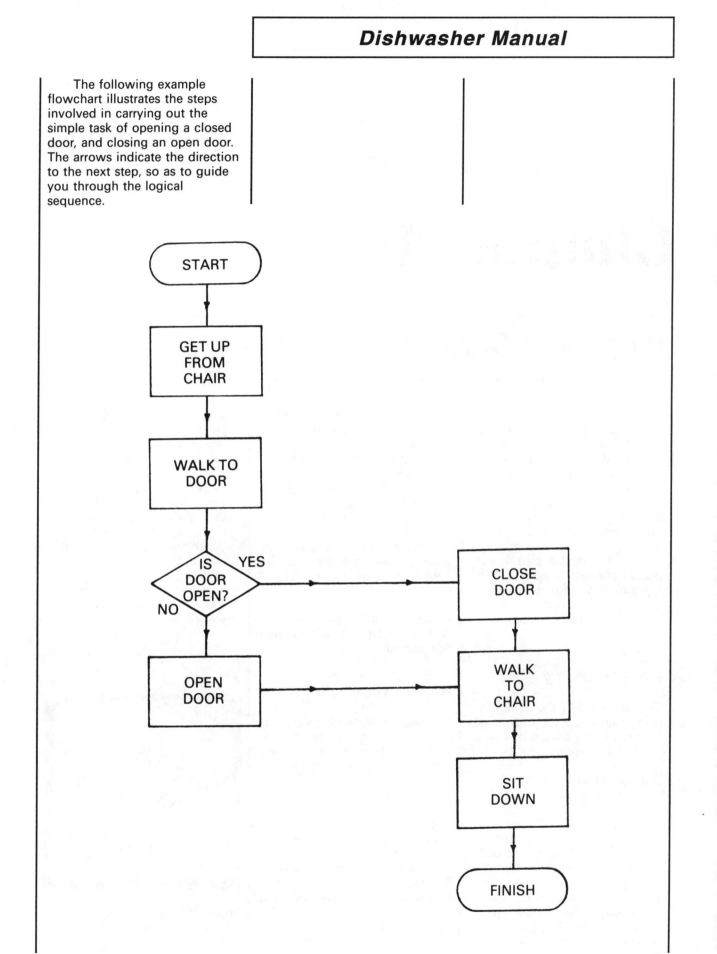

Chapter 10

Plugs and Sockets

Problems with your dishwasher may not always be the result of a failure of the item itself but with the electrical supply to it via the socket. A three-pin socket must have a Live supply, a Neutral return and a sound Earth path. When the plug is inserted in the socket, a firm contact must be made at all three points. If the live or neutral pins of the plug or connection point within the socket fail to make adequate contact or are free to move, localised heating will occur within the socket.

Problem spotting

Tell tale signs of this type of fault often show themselves as;
1. Burn marks around one or both entry points on the socket.
2. Plug hot to the touch after use of appliance in that socket.
3. Pungent smell from socket when appliance is in use.
4. Pitting and burn marks on and around the pins of the plug.
5. Radio interference to nearby equipment caused by internal arcing within the socket creating spurious radio emissions. These may pass along the ring main to hi-fi units, etc.
6. Intermittent operation of the appliance being used.
7. Failure of the fuse in the plug. In this instance, this is not caused by a fault within the appliance but by heat being transferred through the live pin and into the fuse which fails by over-heating.

All these conditions are more likely in appliances which draw a high current.

Why does it happen?

The reasons for such problems are various and may be caused by one or a combination of any of those listed below:

1. Repeated use of the socket, opening up the contact points within the socket. In other words general wear and tear.
2. Poor quality socket or plug.
3. Loose pins on plug.
4. The use of a double adaptor.

This can cause a poor connection purely by the weight of cables and plugs pulling the adaptor partially out of the wall socket. Worse still is allowing a number of high-current-draw appliances to be run through one socket thus causing overloading. Examples might be a washing machine and dishwasher. Whenever possible, avoid the use of adaptors by provision of an adequate number of sockets and do not exceed 3 kW load on any single socket.

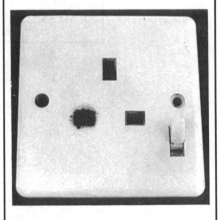

Socket highlighting overheating. Both plug and socket will require replacing.

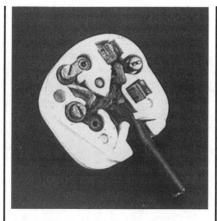

Internal view of severe burnout caused by poor connection to terminal. A new plug is required and the cable cut back to sound wire or renewed.

Incorrectly fitted plug. Wiring bunched and not trimmed to right lengths. Ensure all plugs are fitted correctly.

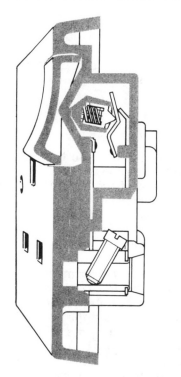

Internal view of 13 amp socket.

Typical resilient plugs which can stand up to rugged use without cracking.

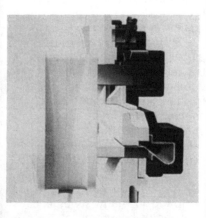

Internal cut away of quality socket showing plug pin contact points.

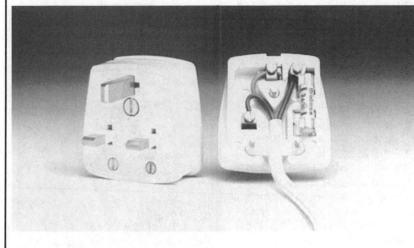

High quality three-pin plug ideal for home appliances.

Always look for the ASTA sign when purchasing electrical fittings.

5. Use of a multi-point extension lead when the total load on the trailing socket can easily exceed the safe 3 kW load of the single socket.

Rectification

First, DO NOT use the socket until the problem has been rectified. If the socket is found to be showing any of the previously described faults, it must be renewed completely. If it is a single socket it may be wise to have a double socket fitted as a replacement. Numerous DIY books describe the renewal of sockets so I won't duplicate the instructions here. Suffice it to say that caution should be exercised when tackling socket renewal. When buying a replacement socket, make sure it is a good quality one as there are many of dubious quality to be found. Price is a good indicator of quality in this field.

It is advisable to renew all plugs that have been used in the faulty socket because damage may have been done to the plug. It is possible, of course, that a faulty plug damaged the socket. To continue using the old plugs could result in premature failure of your new unit.

As with sockets, plugs can be found in many styles and qualities. While some of the poorer quality plugs may prove to be reliable on low current consumption items like lamps, TV and radios, they may not be so good for your dishwasher. Although British Standards do apply to these items, quality does vary considerably. When buying plugs and sockets, go to outlets that can give advice and that carry a good selection. This will allow you to compare quality and build of the products. Look for the ASTA mark which proves that the design and manufacture has been approved by the Association of Short Circuit

Testing Authorities. Replacement fuses should also carry this mark.

The earth

All of the faults mentioned previously relate to the 'live' supply and neutral return on the socket, the plug or both. There is, of course, a third pin. Although it takes no active part in the operation of the appliance, it is, however, the most important connection of all. The function of the earth system is explained in 'Basics – electrical'. Products that have three core cable must have the yellow and green earth wire securely connected to the earth pin of the plug or pin marked E.

The earth path of an appliance can be checked easily using a simple test meter (*see* Electrical Circuit Testing). Remember, a path of low resistance is required from all items within the product that are linked into the earth path via the yellow and green cable.

Note: The earth path of an appliance from its exposed metal parts to the earth pin of the plug should be a maximum of 1 ohm (BS3456).

Checking the socket will require the use of an earth loop test meter which needs to be operated correctly. As these meters are expensive and problems could be encountered with distribution boards fitted with an RCCD, it is advisable to have these tests done by a qualified electrical contractor. A simple plug-in tester like the one shown can be found in most good electrical shops and DIY outlets. This is most useful for checking the socket for reverse polarity. In other words, it will show whether a socket has been incorrectly wired. An incorrectly wired socket can still work and outwardly give no sign of any problem. This type of fault is dangerous and not uncommon. The plug-in tester also indicates if an earth path is

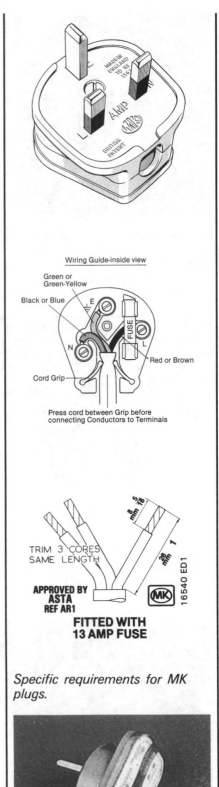

Wiring Guide-inside view

Green or Green-Yellow

Black or Blue

Red or Brown

Cord Grip

Press cord between Grip before connecting Conductors to Terminals

TRIM 3 CORES SAME LENGTH

APPROVED BY ASTA REF AR1

16540 ED1

FITTED WITH 13 AMP FUSE

Specific requirements for MK plugs.

Typical plug in socket tester.

present. However, the quality of the earth in the socket is not shown. That is to say, it may have a very high resistance but would still allow the neon of the tester to light. If the earth resistance is high, remember this may result in a failure to blow the fuse which may cause overheating at the high resistance point or allow a flow of electricity through anything or anyone else that can give a better route to earth.

Plug fitting

The fitting of a plug is often believed to be a straight-forward task that needs little or no explanation. On the contrary, this is an area where many problems are to be found and dangers encountered if the fitting is not done correctly. Do not neglect this most important item.

The following text and photo sequences deal specifically with modern 13A flat-pin plugs. If your property has round-pin plugs and sockets, the indication is that the house wiring may be old and it would be wise to have it checked thoroughly by an expert.

When wiring a plug, it is good practice to leave the earth wire (yellow/green) longer than is necessary merely for connection to the earth terminal to be accomplished. The extra length is taken up in a slight loop shape within the plug. Doing this means that, should the appliance flex be pulled hard accidentally and the plug's cable grip fails to hold, the live and neutral wires will detach from the terminal first, leaving the earth loop intact to provide continued safety cover. The photo of the pillar-type plug shows how the extra little bit of earth wire is contained inside the plug. The post and nut plug shown does not allow for this and the manufacturer

recommends that all wires to be cut to the same length (as shown).

Moulded plugs

Some appliances may be supplied with one-piece moulded 13 amp plugs fitted to the mains cable. If for any reason this type of plug has to be removed (eg to allow the cable to be slotted through a hole in a work surface, or due to damage), because of its moulded construction, it is not possible to take it off in the normal way. The plug has to be cut off with suitable wire cutters and a new plug fitted correctly as shown.

Warning: Any moulded plug removed in this way must be disposed of immediately. It is wise to remove the fuse and to bend the pins of the plug as soon as it is removed to make sure that it cannot be inadvertently plugged into a socket. Do not leave it lying about or dispose of it where children can find it and plug it in.

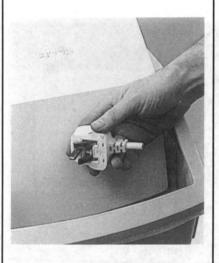

Make sure a moulded plug removed from an appliance cannot be inadvertently plugged in. Remove the fuse and bend the pins.

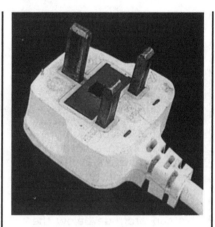

Typical moulded plug.

Do's and Don'ts

DO ensure the cable insulation is removed carefully. Use of the correct wire strippers is recommended.

DO make sure that connections are the right way around.

DO ensure that wires are trimmed to suit plug fixing points and no bunching is present. See poorly fitted plugs illustrations.

DO make sure that all connections are tight and no strands of wire are left protruding from terminals. To prevent this, twist the strands together as shown, prior to fitting.

DO make sure that the cord grip is fitted correctly around the outer insulation only.

DO ensure correct rating of fuse is used to suit appliance.

DO ensure the plug top/cover fits tightly and securely with no cracks or damage present.

DO NOT damage the inner core of wires when removing the outer or inner insulation. If you do, cut back and start again.

DO NOT fit tinned ends of cables into plugs. Some manufacturers tin (dip in solder) the end of the exposed inner conductors. The tinned/soldered end, if fitted to the plug, will work loose and cause problems associated with loose connections. Although tight when fitted, constant pressure over a long period will compress the soft solder resulting in a loose joint. A second problem associated with tinned conductors is the excessive length of exposed inner wire which the manufacturer usually provides. This can protrude below the cord clamp fixing point or force the cable to bunch within the plug to allow the cord clamp to clamp the outer insulation only. Both of these practices are dangerous and must be avoided. Always cut cable lengths to suit the plug. If this poor method of fitting is found on an appliance it must be corrected immediately.

DO NOT allow strands of wire to protrude from any fixing points.

DO NOT fit incorrect fuse ratings. Always match fuses to appliances and observe the manufacturer's instructions.

DO NOT reuse overheated or damaged plugs.

DO NOT by-pass the internal fuse.

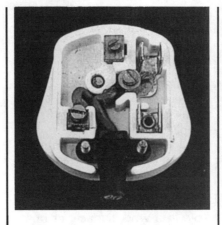

Wiring incorrectly bunched into plug to allow cord grip to hold outer sheath.

Shown are just three of the many instances of how badly a plug can be fitted. The plugs shown are actual examples which were removed from appliances in use. DO NOT use equipment unless the plug is fitted correctly.

Wiring not cut to correct length. As a result the cord grip is fixed across inner wires not outer sheath.

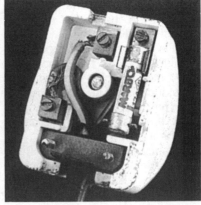

Conductor wire protruding from plug pins.

NOTE: All of the above photographs are used to illustrate the lack of attention to safety to this small but vital component. Always fit plugs correctly and safely. To give further assistance, a step-by-step photo guide for the two types of plug is given overleaf.

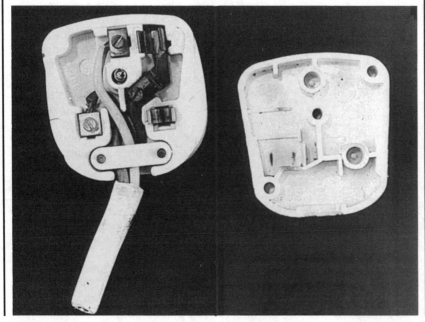

Wiring a plug – pillar type

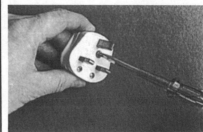

1. Remove the screw that holds the plug top/cover in position, taking care not to lose it.

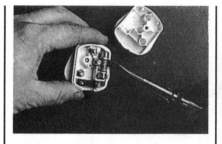

2. Ease the fuse from position (if using a screwdriver, take care not to damage it).

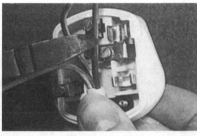

5. Offer the wiring to the plug base with the outer sheath in its correct position resting in the cord clamp area. Next, cut the inner cables to suit, allowing ½ in (13 mm) past the fixing point. Don't forget to allow a little extra on the earth cable to form a slight loop.

8. Fit each wire into its correct pillar and tighten each screw ensuring that it grips the conductor firmly (with thin wires it will help if they are folded over on themselves first). Make sure the wire fits up to the insulation shoulder and no wires or strands protrude from the pillar.

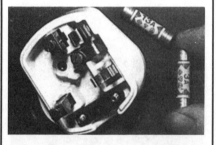

3. Check that the fuse supplied with the plug is of the correct rating for the appliance. Many plugs are supplied with 13 amp fuse already fitted, but do not be tempted to use it unless it is right. In this instance a 3 amp fuse was required.

6. Carefully remove ¼ in (6 mm) of insulation from the end of each wire. This must be done with care to avoid damaging or cutting any strands of the conductor.

9. Fit the cord clamp over the outer sheath and screw it firmly into position while being careful not to strip the threads of the plastic grip.

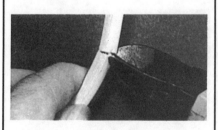

4. Carefully remove the outer cable sheath to expose the inner wires. If damage should occur to the inner wires in the process, cut back and start again.

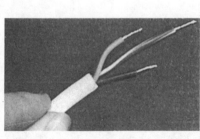

7. Twist the strands of each wire securely together. Make sure there are no loose strands.

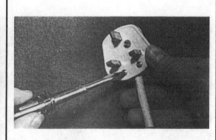

10. Before refitting the top/cover, double check all fixings. Ensure the wiring is seated and routed neatly and is not under stress or bunched. Fit the correct rated fuse, making sure that it is firmly and securely positioned.

*11. With top/cover refitted
tighten the securing screw.*

Wiring a plug – post and nut type

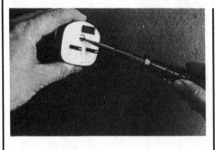

*1. Remove the screw that holds
plug top/cover in position.*

*2. Remove the knurled/slotted
nuts and place them safely in
the top.*

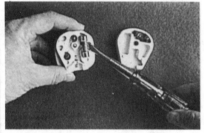

*3. With the plug top/cover
removed, the fuse can be eased
from its position. If using a
screwdriver, take care not to
damage the fuse.*

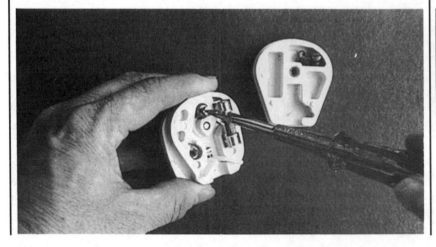

*4. Check that the fuse supplied
with the plug is of the correct
rating for the appliance. Many
plugs are supplied with 13 amp
fuse already fitted but do not be
tempted to use it unless it is
right. In this instance a 13 amp
fuse was required.*

*5. Carefully remove 1¼ in
(32 mm) of the cable sheath to
expose the inner wires. If
damage should occur to the
inner wires in the process, cut
back and start again.*

*6. Now remove $\frac{9}{16}$ in (15 mm)
of insulation from the end of
each wire. This must be done
with care to avoid damaging or
cutting any strands of the
conductor.*

7. Twist the strands of each wire securely together. Make sure there are no loose strands.

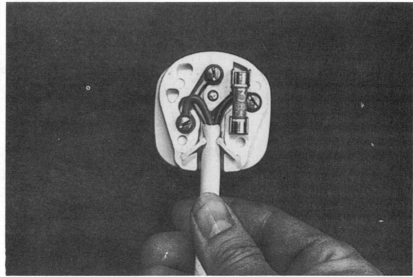

8. The prepared cable can now be inserted into the cord grip ensuring only the outer sheath of the cable is gripped.

10. Securely tighten all three nuts. Ensure that the wire fits up to the insulation shoulder and no wires or strands protrude from the terminal. Before refitting the top/cover, double-check all fixings. Ensure the wiring is seated and routed neatly and is not under stress or bunched. Fit the correct rated fuse, making sure that it is firmly and securely positioned.

11. With top/cover refitted tighten the securing screw. This type has a captive screw with a shockproof washer to prevent it working loose during use.

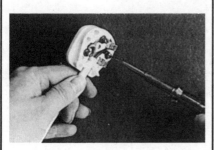

9. Fit each conductor (wire) to its correct terminal. Make sure each is fitted in a clockwise direction otherwise it will be pushed out as the nut is tightened. Ensure only the conductor is gripped and not the outer insulation.

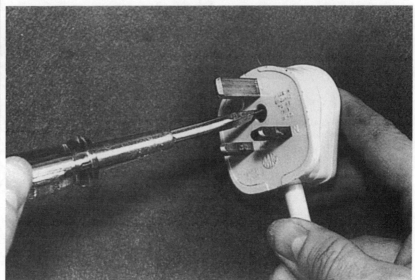

PLUGS AND SOCKETS <u>FLOWCHART</u>

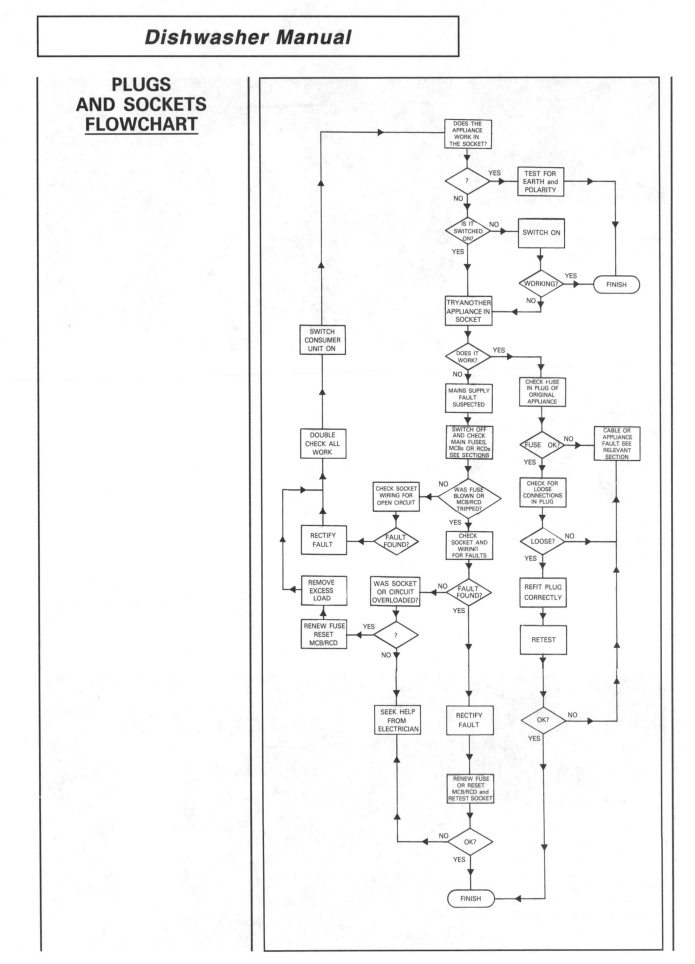

Chapter 11

Determining the fault

Throughout the manual, flowcharts are used to aid the fault finding process. The location of faults will become much easier as you become more conversant with your machine. i.e. Through regular servicing of your machine before faults have arisen.

Selecting the correct flowchart for the job will be made easier if it is remembered that faults fall into three main categories: mechanical, electrical and chemical.

Mechanical faults will normally become apparent by a change in the usual operational noise level of the machine. i.e. A high pitched squealing noise on a washing cycle may indicate a bearing fault on the wash pump. A banging noise from inside the cabinet may indicate a worn spray arm bearing which would allow the arm to wobble excessively.

Electrical faults fall into two major categories:
Component faults – A fault is classed as a component fault when a complete unit has failed. i.e. If the pump, heater, motor, etc. should fail, the fault is said to be a component fault.
Impulse path faults – A fault is classed as an IMPULSE fault when an internal, pre-determined instruction has failed. i.e. If the thermostat does not close or open at the required temperature, or the timer fails to move on after a given time sequence this constitutes an impulse path fault. Simply, this is the failure of the machine to move correctly through its selected programme. An instance of this type of fault is explained below:

The timer supplies power to the heater, but due to a fault in the thermostat circuit, the timer is not supplied with the information that the correct temperature has been reached. Due to this, the timer does not move on, but remains on the heat position and exceeds the selected temperature. It should be noted that there is no fault in the timer, just in one of its impulse paths. A similar fault would arise if the thermostat circuit was O.K., the thermostat closed at the correct temperature, but the timer failed to move on after the correct time had elapsed. This would be a fault of the timer's internal impulse path via its timing mechanism.

Chemical faults are normally associated with the powder being used and will cover such problems as: poor washing, scaling problems, blocking, etc. A comprehensive guide to washing problems and useful hints will be found at the rear of this manual, in the section – *Common causes of poor results and discoloration problems.*

Fault finding reference guide

Machine will not work at all

Basics – electrical chapter
Functional testing
Door safety switches
Timers/programmers

Machine leaks

Emergency procedures
Leaks fault finding
Water level control/pressure systems
Pumps
Door seals
Inlet valve fault finding

Machine will not empty

Emergency procedures
Pumps
Basic plumbing
Wiring harness faults

Machine will not fill/take powder

Functional testing
Inlet valve fault finding
Detergent dispenser

Machine does not wash clean

Check filters
Check spray arms
Common causes of poor wash results
Basic plumbing
Pump

Machine is noisy

Loading
Wash pump
Spray arms
Outlet pump

Machine won't move through programme

Thermostats
Heater
Inlet valve fault finding
Programmer/timer faulty
Wiring harness faults

Machine sticks through programme

Basic plumbing
Pump
Inlet valve fault finding
Heater
Door safety switches
Programmer/timer
Wiring harness faults

Machine blows fuses

Emergency procedures
Basics – electrical chapter
Low insulation
Wiring harness faults

The lists below the main fault headings indicate the sequence with which they should be examined.

Shown is a simplified flowchart of the operation described on page 39

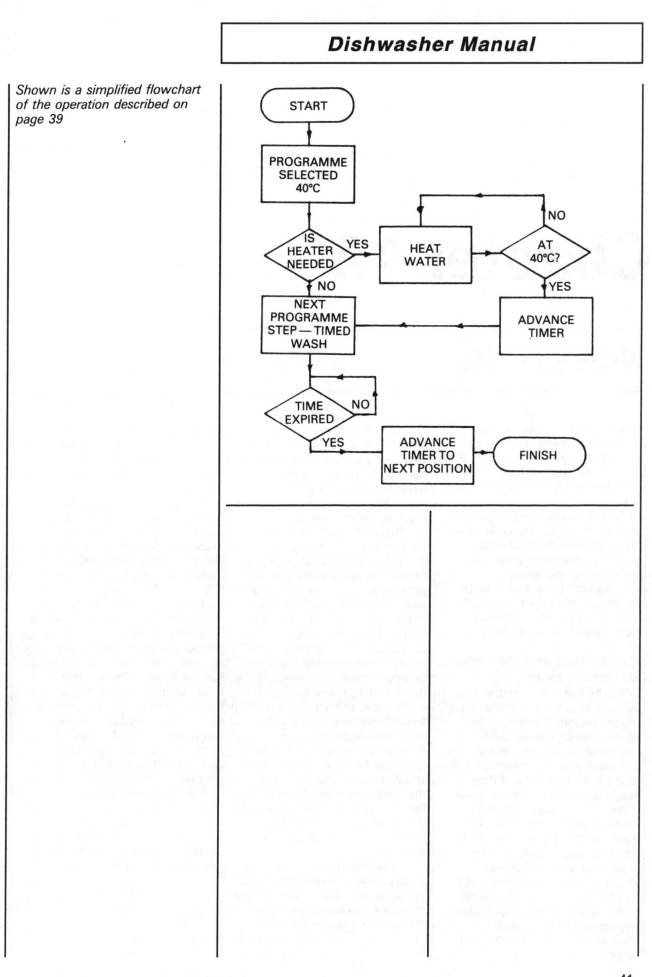

Chapter 12

Noise faults

Noise can be one of the first signs that something is going wrong with your dishwasher. It is quite common for noise faults to be ignored initially, but then over a period of time, they are accepted as the norm. Obviously, it is advisable to investigate any noise as soon as it is heard, hopefully avoiding larger problems in the future.

As with other faults, noise faults become easier to identify and locate the more conversant you are with your machine.

Noise faults and their most common causes

A rhythmical bumping/banging noise during a wash cycle could simply be bad loading of the dishes, which can be easily remedied by turning the machine off, waiting a few seconds for the spray arms to stop, and then repositioning the offending items. (Note: it is important to pause before opening the door as the spray arms are still rotating and could possibly spray very hot water out of the machine). Alternatively, this noise could be caused by loose or worn spray arm mounts which would allow the spray arm to wobble excessively and catch the load baskets. (see *Spray arms*).

A high pitched squealing would indicate bearing wear of the wash pump or outlet pump, possibly caused by water penetration due to worn shaft seals, etc. A similar noise can be made by worn spray arm bearings. This can often be confirmed by excessive movement on its shaft. If you experience any difficulty in determining whether the noise is emanating from the circulation pump bearing or the spray arms, simply secure the spray arms to the top and bottom baskets to prevent them rotating, (this can be done simply with tape). If the noise is still present during the wash cycle, this will then confirm a seal or bearing fault on the main circulation motor or impeller. Conversely, if the noise has stopped, then a fault on the spray arm is indicated. Noise on the outlet cycle would indicate a fault with the bearings or seal on the outlet pump. More details can be found in the relevant *Pumps* sections.

A whistling type noise could signify a more unusual fault with the water inlet either at the valve or the air brake system. Simple cleaning or a reduction in pressure at the isolation tap could rectify this. (See *Inlet valves, Air break systems* and *Steam vents*).

If large items are allowed to get past the main filters (this may happen if care is not taken when they are removed for cleaning), they may foul the wash pump impeller. Prolonged usage with an item lodged in this area will seriously damage the impeller, and if it jams completely, the whole motor could be affected. To avoid this happening, take great care when removing filters and make sure they are re-fitted securely. Small spoons or cocktail sticks are the most popular items to find their way into the filters. In the event of broken dishes in the machine, ensure that all the pieces are removed, especially if it is glass, as glass in water is extremely difficult to detect. Take care. **Note:** such accidents should not happen if a little care is taken in loading the machine. All modern machines are extremely gentle on all articles of glass, china, etc., but having said that, it is advisable to check the suitability of any item before putting it in the dishwasher.

Chapter 13

Door safety switches

All dishwashers have at least one door safety switch. These are generally very simple ON/OFF switches, and although their size and shape differs with different makes and models, their function remains the same. They are normally "open" switches and will only make contact when the door of the dishwasher is correctly closed or latched. If the door is inadvertently opened during the normal cycle, the switch will return to its normally open position. The door safety micro switch is normally on the live feed to the timer and will therefore effectively cut off the power to all parts of the machine. **Note:** Opening the door mid cycle whilst the machine is running can be dangerous. Although the power is cut off, the spray arms continue to rotate for a few seconds. If the door is opened quickly the hot water in the machine may spray out. Pause before opening the door for any reason and keep your face away from the opening when you do so.

For extra safety, the switch is often operated by an elongated arm. The position of the switch can vary – some are mounted in the door whilst others may be mounted in the main body at the

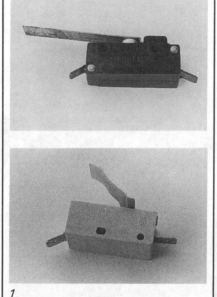

1.
Typical door safety switches. Note the operating arms. As the switch carries all the power it is liable to overheating problems due to poor connections or contacts.

2.
Peg operated machine.

3.
Latch operated switch. Note also the overheated connection of this machine.

latch position. Some are actuated by a protruding peg mounted either on the door or body of the machine. When the door is closed, the peg enters into a recess and actuates the switch at a given position.

On other machines, the switch is an integral part of the handle and latch system, and is actuated only when the latch is in its correct position. Adjustment is possible on both variants. Under no circumstances should

4.
Internal view of door showing position of door safety switch.

safety switches be by-passed. The switches themselves often fail due to the amount of operations during normal use and especially if the user has a habit of opening the door when the machine is running.

If the machine is dead, a simple check is to listen for the audible click of the micro switch when you open and close the door (WITH THE MACHINE ISOLATED). This would give only an indication of failure and a thorough check would be needed to verify the fault.

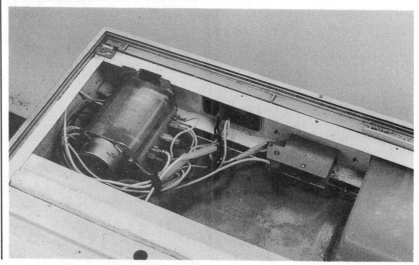

▲ *Close-up of latch mechanism. Early Indesit machine.*

Close-up of recessed switch position.

Chapter 14

Door seals

Because of the action and the force of water within the dishwasher, it is important to have a water tight seal around all edges of the load compartment door. This sealing effect is achieved by a moulded rubber strip around the outer edge of the load compartment opening, and a second strip fixed along the lower edge of the door inner liner. When the door is closed and latched correctly, enough force is exerted to form a secure water tight seal.

There are as many variations of the extruded rubber seals as there are makes of dishwashers, but all are there for the same purpose.

Normal wear and tear can give rise to leaking, especially evident at the corners. Always ensure that the seal and its corresponding contact area are clean and free from food particles as the seal depends on a good contact area. Regular cleaning of the seal and contact area will greatly extend the life of the seal. Before renewing the door seal, always check the levelness of the machine, water level, correct quality and dosage of detergent, seal and contact area and check that the door is closing securely and tightly on the seal.

Adjustment or cleaning maybe all that is required to cure the problem. If these methods fail, change both seals, making sure that you obtain the correct seal for your particular make and model of machine as shape, size and thickness vary greatly. A point to watch out for is that the load baskets do not foul the seal when they are pushed in and out. On some models, this can cause problems and may require adjustment to the basket height or position.

The fixings of the outer seal can be of two types:
A.   A moulded rubber strip with a solid flat edge that is held in place by a separate metal/plastic outer fixing secured in place by screws. To fit a new seal, first loosen the fixing screws and pull the old seal free. Refitting is a simple reversal of the removal procedure but make sure the seal is not stretched or forms loops or bumps by being slack.
B.   Simply a push fit into a preformed recess (some maybe lightly glued into the recess). To remove, simply pull from one end to free it from the recess). When refitting, start at one end leaving about 20 mm protruding out of the bottom. Push the seal firmly into its position. Do this carefully

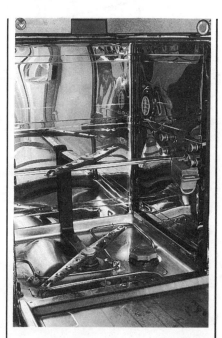

Outer door seal.

in stages and avoid stretching or leaving it to go slack. If care is not taken at this stage, the new seal will not function properly. When in position all the way round, press again firmly with your fingers to ensure a snug fit. If the seal appears loose, check

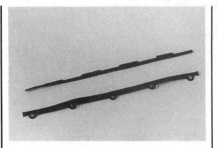

Two types of lower door seal.

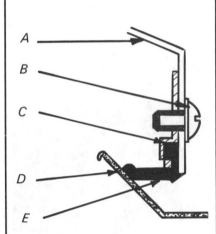

A

B

C

D

E

for stretching and adjust as necessary. Should the new seal simply be a loose fit in a metal recess, tap the recess edge slightly to narrow the recess width.

The bottom seal can be either fixed by screws or riveted into position. The removal is by slackening the fixing screws or drilling of the holding rivets. When refitting, it is best to start at the middle and work outward, at the same time making sure the seal is positioned correctly. The use of a self-locking wrench as a third hand can be most useful for this job. Some machines simply secure the lower seal by allowing it to fit over the lower lip of the load compartment – these are the easiest of all seals to renew.

Fig. 4 Lower door seal fitting
A. Door inner
B. Fixing bolt or rivet
C. Inner clamp plate
D. Bottom panel of load
*   compartment*
E. Formed rubber seal in correct
*   position*

Chapter 15

Spray arms

What are they?

The spray arms are the units that direct and distribute the wash and rinse water to all parts of the load compartment. Most machines have two spray arms and some have more. The top and bottom spray arms may look the same but take care not to mix them up and refit them incorrectly.

How do they work?

Supported on a central pivot point, both top and bottom spray arms are free to rotate. Water, under pressure from the main circulation pump, is directed to or fed directly to them both. Along the upper face of each spray arm there are slots that are slightly angled. Each end of the spray arms have corresponding but opposing holes in them. The angle and position of these holes are so aligned that the water supplied at pressure to the arm is forced out and gives a driving momentum. This in turn causes the arms to rotate as the water is sprayed from them. This movement, combined with detergent and heating is how the dishwasher cleans the wash load.

What are they made of?

The material used for spray arms is either plastic or stainless steel. The means of supplying water to the top spray arm differs as some are fed directly and others are indirectly fed a jet of water from above or below. See diagram showing a top jet fed system. A bottom jet system would simply invert the funnel shaped catch point.

For the machine to work efficiently and effectively the spray arms must be:
A. Free to rotate on both its pivot points and not be jammed by items protruding above or below its position.
B. All the slots within the arm must be clear of debris to allow the jets to operate correctly.
C. Must be sound – look for splits or cracks along the seams or joints. These may be hard to spot but when under pressure

Fig. 5. A typical spray arm

they will open up and reduce the power to the arm.

Although the unit may look simple in itself, if it is not maintained and cleaned regularly or its rotation has been impeded in any way, the following problems such as poor wash, poor rinses, leaving food on items and noise could result.

Some machines can be programmed to vary the pressure to the stop spray arm for use on delicate items. This is a relatively simple operation but remember to reset to normal following the special wash procedure.

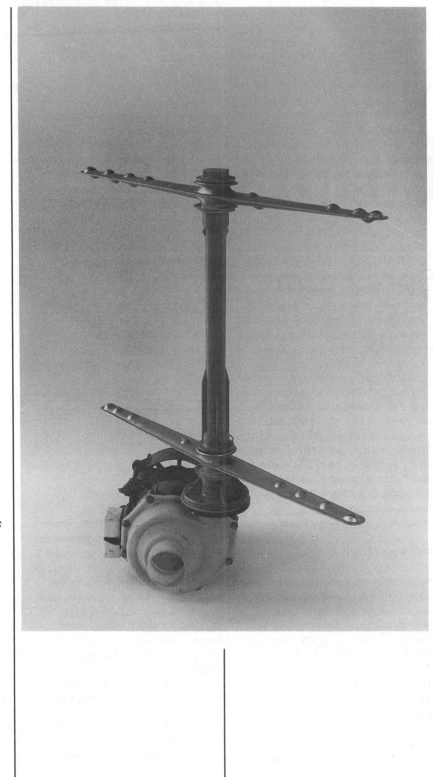

View of spray arm system. In this instance the top spray arm is fed by a central column. Many variations of supplying the top spray arm can be found. Check for wear on spray arm bearings and ensure washers or spacers are in good condition.

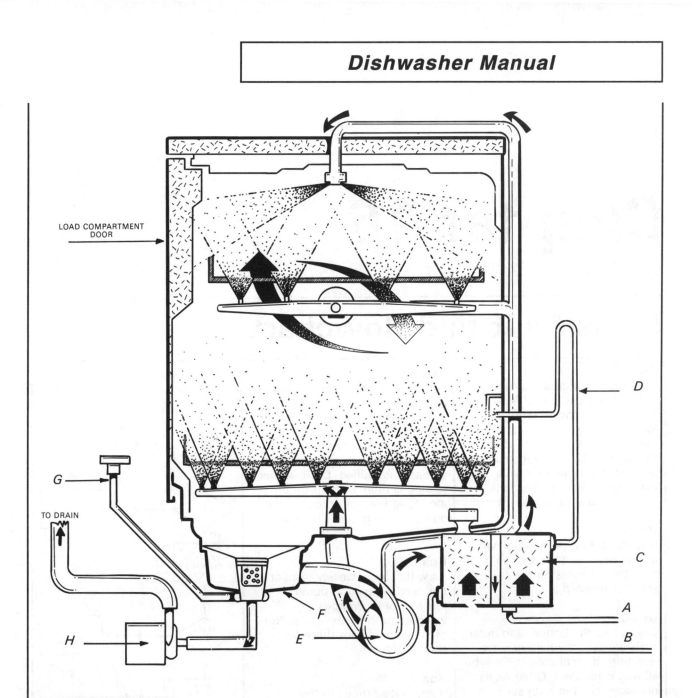

LOAD COMPARTMENT
DOOR

G

TO DRAIN

H

F

E

D

C

A

B

Fig. 6 Typical water flow in a
dishwasher

Water inlet is via points (A) for
normal inlet and (B) for
regeneration sequence. (C) is the
water softener unit with outlet
(D) to load compartment. (E) is
the main circulation pump
supplying both top and bottom
spray arms and jet in this
instance (means of supply may
vary, ie jet of water or direct
supply as shown). Supply of
water is drawn from sump unit
(F). Pressure system and switch
(G) control water level (could
also be float system). Outlet of
water to drain is by outlet pump
(H) via supply from sump.

Chapter 16

Leaks fault find flowchart

Box 1
It is essential that dishwashers are within 2 degrees of level. Before commencing with any leak checking, ensure that the machine is as near level as possible. Refer to the instruction booklet that came with your machine on how this is done for your particular machine.

Box 2
Inspect and clean the door seals at this point, at the same time look for flat spots on the seal, splits or perishing.

Box 3
Check that the bottom and outer seals are securely held in place. Refitting the seal correctly maybe all that is required. Other faults normally result in both seals being replaced.

Box 4
Inspect the air break unit. Blockages in this system can result in leaking only when the machine fills. Both main wash and rinses can be affected. Although the spillage maybe small on each fill, after main fill and four rinses, the pool of water can become quite large.

Removal of a side panel is usually required to gain access to this unit. Small scale blockages in the inlet jets can cause the water to be deflected from its normal course. Check and clean thoroughly.

Box 5
The outlet pump may conceal a shaft seal leak. Close inspection of this unit is required. If the machine has had a leak for sometime which has gone unnoticed, a shaft seal leak can be easily identified. Corrosion or scaling is often evident on the mounting bracket or rear of the pump housing. See Chapter 27 on *Pumps*.

Box 6
As with Box 5, closely inspect the main circulation pump looking for discharges or weeping in the same areas. Noise often accompanies these larger shaft seal leaks.

Box 7
Sump hose fittings to the sump vary – some are clip fitted and others are grommet fitted. Check clip and grommet and seal if in doubt. Hose to spray arms will require very close inspection as these hoses are under high pressure from the circulation pump, and small holes or ill-fitting clips on them can result in very large leaks. Such high pressure leaks are unsafe as they can spray water over the machines electrics when in use. As with all leaks, trace and rectify before further problems arise and do not compromise safety.

Box 8
Check this hose for loose fitting,

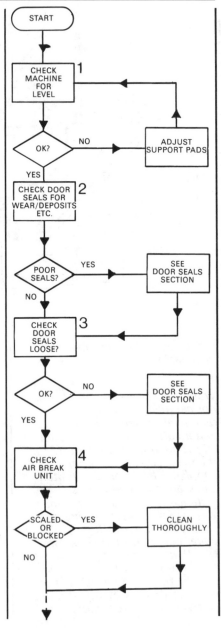

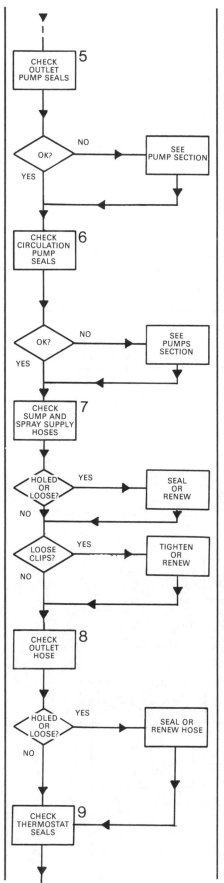

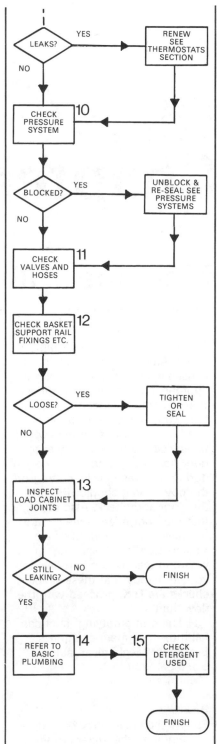

perishing and kinks and especially look for rubbing against other hoses or panels. Check the whole length of hose and renew if in doubt.

Box 9
Look for ill-fitting grommets or discharges from them. Perished grommets should be renewed.

Box 10
Pressure system faults can give rise to leaks that range from small to major. Always check thoroughly and clean all pressure hoses and vessels. This also applies to float systems. See: *Pressure systems and float systems.*

Box 11
The hoses and clips on the inlet valves should now be checked in conjunction with Chapter 18 *Inlet valves:* On earlier valves there is a slight chance that the top of the valve can split. This is often shown by a small brown rust patch on the top of the valve.

Box 12
The rails supporting both upper and lower basket runners may be fixed to the cabinet sides with bolts or self-tapping screws. These fixings are sealed but over long periods of use, may become loose. When in use the pressure within the cabinet will force water past and result in a tricky leak to locate. The outer panel of the affected side may have to be removed to gain access to the nuts of any fixing bolts.

Box 13
The inner load compartment is made up of separate panels or mouldings. On rare occasions a split or breakdown of the joint may occur. If all other tests prove to be O.K. yet the leak persists, check all seals and joints thoroughly. Curing such problems can be tricky, but if encountered, small faults may be rectified by using an epoxy glue to coat the affected section.

Box 14/15
If the fault persists at this point, re-inspect plumbing and ensure it corresponds with the Basics – plumbing, Chapter 6. If this should not prove to be at fault, Box 15 directs you to powder used. See: *Common causes of poor washing results.*

Chapter 17

Machine will not empty

This is one of the most common faults. Although inconvenient, it is usually remedied if the fault is approached in a logical manner. Before commencing with the following sequence of the flow chart, a few simple checks would be advisable. Make sure that the door has not sprung slightly open during the wash cycle, cutting off the power as it should. Re-latch the door and check. Also check that the door micro switch has not failed as this would give a similar situation depending on where in the cycle it had failed. If you are happy that these simple checks are O.K. proceed with the flowchart.

The 'not emptying' fault can fall into three main categories. Blockage, Mechanical fault or Electrical fault.

Box 1
Follow the emergency procedure for removing the water already trapped inside the machine.

Box 2
Check the outlet and sump hoses, as well as the outlet filter. If a blockage or a kink has been found, remove it and refit the pipe(s) and filter.

MACHINE WILL NOT EMPTY FLOWCHART

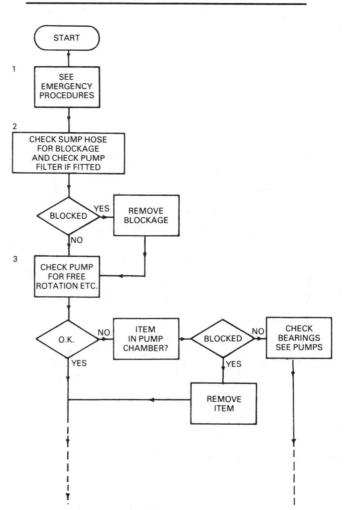

Box 3

The pump is located at the machine end of the outlet hose, and junction of the sump hose, or an integral part of the sump moulding (on some machines such as Zanussi the impeller is held on by a nut and both nut and impeller have to be removed before the pump body can be withdrawn). The small chamber should be checked for blockages, the impeller should be checked for free rotation, and that it hasn't come adrift from its mounting to the pump motor shaft. If the impeller is found to be adrift from the shaft, this would give rise to no water being pumped although the motor itself would run. A quick check of the connection of the shaft and impeller would be to hold the shaft whilst trying to turn the impeller. If all is well they should only turn in unison. Remember to turn anti-clockwise, or the impeller will unscrew from the shaft. If a fault is found at this point, refer to Chapter 27.

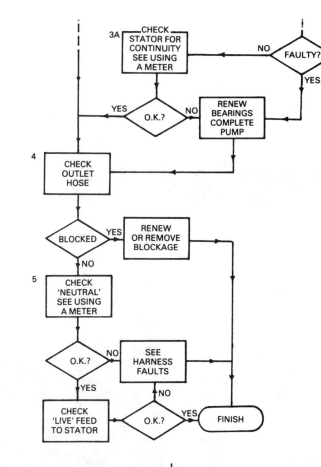

Box 3A

If NO blockage is found in the section above, and the bearings are not suspected, the stator continuity of the pump windings must be checked. Please refer to the chapter *Electrical circuit testing (Using a meter)*.

Box 4

At this point, the outlet hose should be checked again. An internal blockage such as fat deposits can be very difficult to see. The best method of checking this is to connect it to the hose of a domestic tap, observing the flow of water.

Box 5

The final step is to check the wiring harness connection. Please refer to: *Wiring harness faults*, Chapter 32.
Note: On machines that only have one motor for both outlet and circulation, similar faults can occur. See: Chapter 27 *(Induction motor pumps)*.

Chapter 18

Inlet valves

Inlet valve fault finding

We deal here with several of the most common faults reported: not taking powder, not filling at all and not filling in certain parts of the programme. Please refer to the flowchart to be found later in this Chapter.

Water inlet valves fitted to the dishwasher operate in the same way as those used in automatic clothes washers. A solenoid coil of some 3-5000Ω (3—5KΩ) resistance when energised (i.e. supplied with power), creates a strong magnetic field at its centre. This field attracts, up into the coil, a soft iron rod or plunger, and will hold it in that position as long as power is supplied to the coil. When power is cut off (de-energised) from the coil, a spring at the top of the plunger recess returns it to its resting position.

Single valve: Red for hot supply, white for cold supply. (Note: This valve has an earth tag).

Double valves: Cold supply only. Right side for main fill, left for softener regeneration cycle. (Note restrictor on left-hand opening).

Triple valve: Generally cold supply. May also have restrictor on one outlet for regeneration cycle.

How does it work?

Shown here in detail are the two states of the water valve.

Fig. 7a The de-energised valve (at rest – no power supplied)

With no power supplied to the solenoid coil (a), the soft iron core (b) is pressed firmly onto the centre hole of the flexible diaphragm by spring (c). As chamber (d) is only at atmospheric pressure and the water is at least 4 lbs p.s.i. (somewhat higher), pressure is exerted on the top of the diaphragm*, effectively closing it tight. The greater the water pressure the greater the closing effect of the valve and, therefore no water will flow.

*The pressure on top of the diaphragm is via a small bleed hole marked (e). It is essential that this very small hole is not obstructed. Though very small, it is a major factor in the correct operation of these types of pressure operated valves.

Fig. 7b The energised valve (power supplied to it)

When power is supplied to the solenoid coil, the resulting magnetic attraction of the coil overcomes the power of the spring (c) and pulls the plunger up into the coil centre. This allows an imbalance of pressure to occur by exposing the centre hole of the diaphragm. The imbalance lifts the flexible diaphragm and allows water to flow into chamber (d), thus water flow is achieved.

It is easier for the water to lift the diaphragm than to balance the pressure by flowing through the very small bleed hole. Any enlargement or blockage of this vital bleed hole will render the valve inoperative.

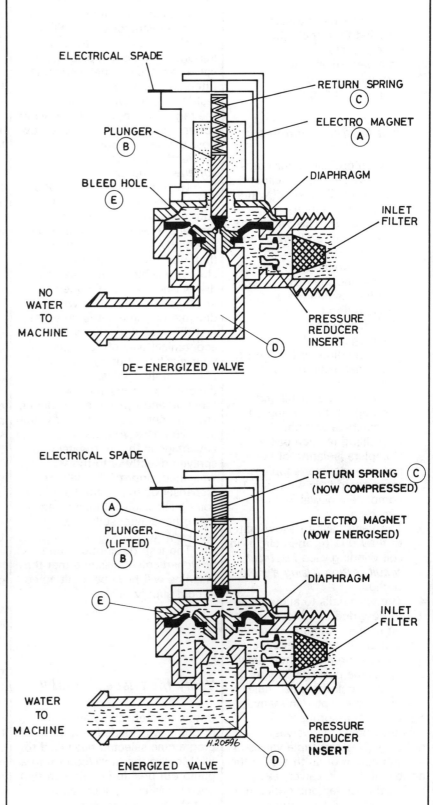

DE-ENERGIZED VALVE

ENERGIZED VALVE

Main benefits of such valves

1. The higher the pressure supplied to it, the tighter the valve will close.
2. Cost is relatively low.
3. Very reliable to use.
4. Simple to change if faulty.

Typical faults to watch for

1. As with ordinary house taps, the valve seat may wear and allow a small trickle of water to pass even when de-energised. This will cause the machine to fill when not in use if the taps are left turned on over a long period of time and the machine will over fill, resulting in a possible flood.
2. The valve, when de-energised, will fail to allow the plunger to return to its normal resting/closed position. This problem will cause severe over-fill and flooding. Note: Turning off the machine will not stop the over filling in such cases. Complete isolation of both power and water supply is required and, as with step 1, complete renewal will be necessary.
3. The valve fails to allow water to flow due to open circuit in coil winding. See *Electrical circuit testing (Using a meter)* section.
4. The valve fails to allow water to flow due to a blocked filter on its inlet. Carefully remove and clean. Do not allow any particle, no matter how small to escape past the filter as it could block the bleed hole.

Water valves come in many sizes and an assortment of shapes, from single valves, double valves and triple valves or a combination of all three. On the double and triple valves, each solenoid operates one outlet from a common inlet. Unfortunately, a fault on one coil or one output will generally mean a complete renewal of the whole valve assembly, as individual spare parts are not available. Note: On dishwashers with double or triple valves, a restrictor will be fitted to one of the valve outlets. It is important that any replacement valve has this internal restrictor fitted. The valve with the restrictor is for water supply to the regeneration side of the water softener unit, as it requires a slow flow of water to operate efficiently. See *Internal water softeners* chapter.

The water requirement of a dishwasher differs little from the automatic clothes washing machine. However, it is generally agreed by most manufacturers that, unlike the hot and cold fill clothes washing machines, the dishwasher is best plumbed cold water only, unless otherwise directed by the manufacturer. At first this may not seem a very economical way of operating your machine, but by using the cold fill only, (unless otherwise directed), your machine will function and operate much better, and will not waste your hot water for cold rinses. Another advantage is that hot water sprayed directly onto the washload, prior to the detergent dispenser opening, will help fix soiling especially albumen (egg) and other similar soiling on crockery etc.

The test, descriptions and flowcharts given assume that the machine will have been plumbed in cold supply only.

Verify the suspected fault

In this theoretical instance, the machine was loaded and a programme selected but failed to fill. Moving the timer/control to a pump out position confirmed that power was being supplied and that the door safety switch was working. See *Door safety switches* chapter.

Box 1
Reselect wash programme to confirm that machine was originally set and turned on correctly. With the machine properly set.

Box 2
Confirms that, although the machine has electrical feed, no water is entering to begin the filling/washing action.

Box 3
This may seem too obvious to mention, but many an engineer has been called out to find the taps were in the 'OFF' position. This normally brings up the comment that the taps are "never turned off", and in this case it must have been some other devious member of the family or innocent plumber that has done the dirty deed! This comment brings in the cardinal rule that all automatic washing machines and dishwashers should be turned off at their isolation taps when the machine is not in use. This may seem a quite pointless task, but the objective is simple. If an inlet hose should split, or an inlet valve fails to close correctly, a quite disastrous flood could occur. This would not be the case however, if the taps were turned off.

Note: If the machine has a float or pressure actuated flood protection valve as described in Water level control (*pressure section*), it should be checked along with all pivot points and pressure hose connections.

Box 4
By unscrewing the hose from the valve, confirmation of water supply can be easily checked by turning the tap, to which it is connected, ON and OFF, ensuring that the free end of the hose is resting in a suitable container. Failure of water flow could be due to a faulty tap or tap shaft or an internal fault of the supply hose.

Box 5

The checking of the water valve inlet filter can be carried out while the hose is removed for Step 4. Take care not to allow any particles to escape past the fine mesh filter and into the valve. Carefully clean the filter of all scale and debris etc., and replace. Note: The filter can be removed by gently gripping the centre with pliers and pulling it free of the main valve body.

Box 6

Ensure that the water supply to the valve is adequate to operate the valve. See: *Basics – plumbing* chapter.

Box 7 & 8

If the heater is found to be ON when there is no water in the machine, a pressure system fault is indicated and should be checked. Details of this process will be found in the Water level control (*Pressure system*) section. If the heater is in the OFF position when there is no water in the machine, the valve would appear to be suspect. The valve is easily changed by removing the fixing screws and detaching the internal hose/s from the valve. Making a note of the wiring and hose connections that are on the valve, remove them and replace with a new valve assembly by simply reconnecting the hoses and wires in a reverse sequence.

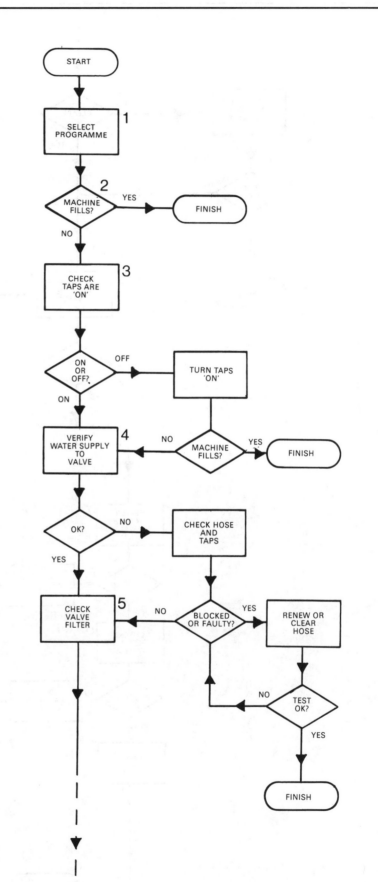

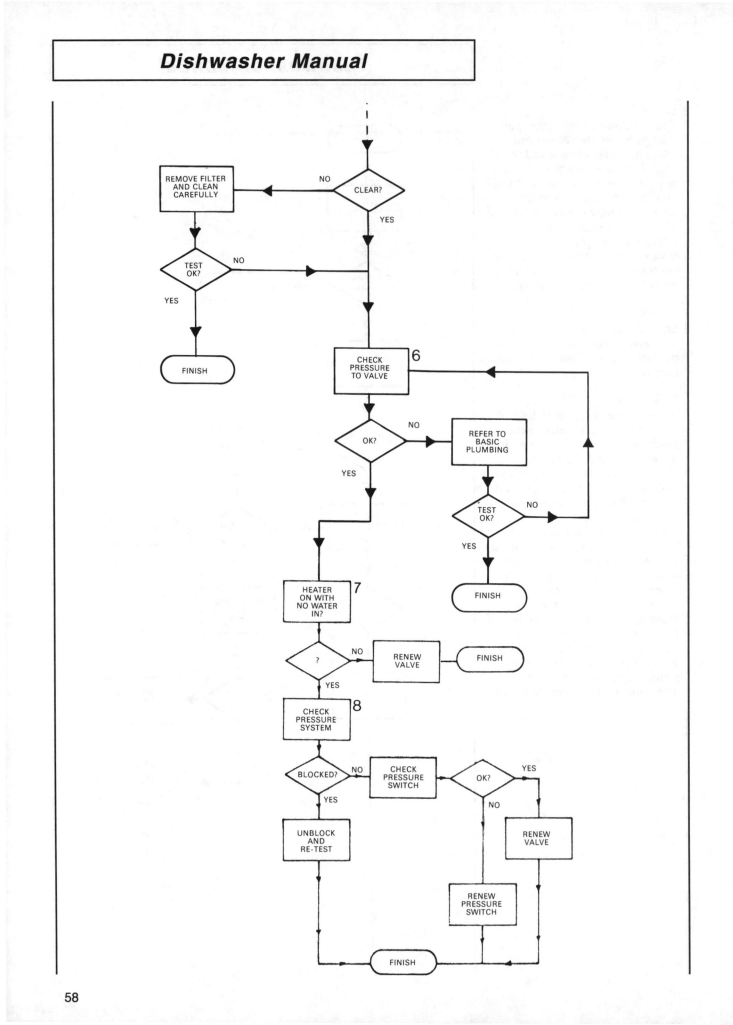

Chapter 19

Air break systems

What is an air break?

An air break is a device to create a gap between the water inlet to the machine and the water within the machine used for the washing and rinsing.

Where is it located?

The location of air breaks differs from machine to machine. The shapes and designs are also varied. Some combine the dual function of air break and steam vent in one unit. To locate the air break system, follow the outlet pipe from the valve or softener unit. If necessary, you may have to remove a side panel of the dishwasher to do this.

What are they for?

Air breaks are essential to create an unbridgeable gap between the clean fresh water from the domestic supply and the soiled water inside the machine. This gap prevents any soiling or wash detergent etc. from going back down the inlet hose and into the house supply. This is a requirement of all water authorities and the air break ensures that this cannot happen under any circumstances.

How does it work?

Although the shape, size, positioning and complexity of air breaks vary greatly, they all use the same principle. The inlet, either direct from the fill valves for ordinary rinsing, or via the softener compartment etc., is formed into a jet of water at the inlet to the air break by its own pressure. The jet is directed across an air gap within the unit to a catchment point, and then on by gravity to the load compartment. If water were to be forced back in the other direction it would be slowed by the design of the unit and unable to jump the gap or be caught by the inlet jet. If the machine overfilled dramatically and reached the height of the unit, the air gap is so designed that it would vent the overfill to the atmosphere, i.e. to flood out of the air gap before making a bridge between the jet and the catchment area.

Problems with air breaks

Generally, air break units are very reliable if at first sight complicated. The units that are

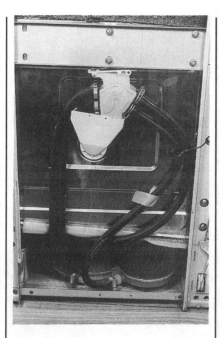

Typical air break system found on dishwashers.

combined with the pressure vessel and steam vents seem especially complicated, but when studied closely are quite simple. The main trouble occurs with blocking and scaling in certain parts of the unit. Both faults can cause water to leak from the air gap. One such fault is at the water inlet points where scaling, although maybe only slight, can cause the jet to spray or become misaligned resulting in water escaping from the air break gap. Careful cleaning and regular checking of the system will prevent most if not all faults. The need to renew the air break system is very unusual, but if it becomes necessary is not a difficult task. Make sure all the hose positions are marked clearly before removal and that they are sealed securely when the new unit is fitted. Some machines may also combine water compartments for the regeneration cycle within the airbreak. These units are easily recognised as they are of a much larger construction.

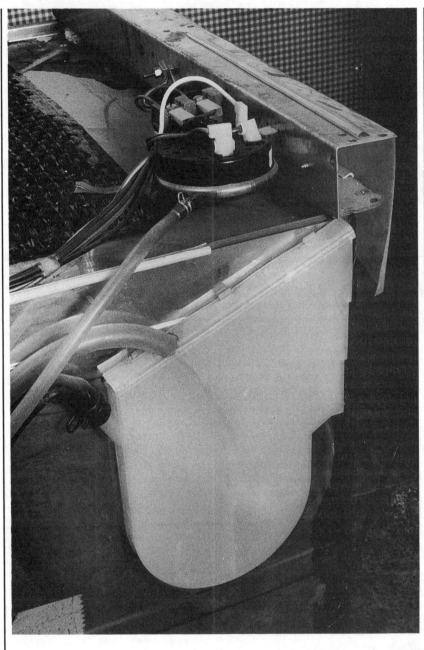

Candy air break system.

Chapter 20

Water level control

There are three ways in which the level of water is controlled in dishwashers:

1. Timed fills, i.e. the timer allows the fill valve a pre-determined time of operation at the end of which it moves on to its next operation regardless of the level reached (such timed fills are often linked to other operations, eg. pre-wash or rinse and hold).
2. Pressure switches and pressure systems similar to those used in automatic clothes washing machines, but operated at much lower trapped air pressures.
3. Float switches are often used either independently or in conjunction with ordinary pressure systems.

Many variations and combinations will be found. What follows is a description of the systems found in most, if not all of today's modern dishwashers. As your machine may contain one or more of the systems it is best that the whole of this chapter be read and a knowledge of all types of systems gained.

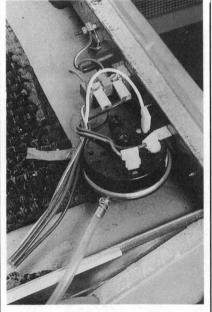

Typical top mounted pressure switch. (Situated beneath lid of machine).

What is a pressure system?

The pressure system governs the level of water in the machine.

Where is it located?

The pressure switch has no standard fixture location. It can be identified as the large circular switch that has several wires and a plastic tube attached to it. Pressure vessels have two distinct designs, and are usually made of rigid plastic. The first type is an integral part of the plastic sump housing, the second is an independent unit usually located to the side of the machine. There is also a pressure hose system. This does the same task as the pressure vessel, and is a part of the flexible sump hose. This will either be grommet-fitted to the lower part of the load compartment or be between the outlet pump and the sump chamber.

How does it work?

The pressure switch does not actually come into contact with water, but uses air pressure trapped within the pressure vessel or pressure hose. When water enters the load compartment and the level rises, it traps a given amount of air in the pressure vessel. As the water in the tub rises, so the pressure of the air in the pressure vessel increases. This pressure is then transferred to a pressure sensitive switch via a small bore flexible tube.

Base mounted pressure switch centre right-hand side (arrowed). **Note:** *When machine is laid over for any reason, ensure that water does not enter the pressure tube. If in doubt always clear the pressure tube prior to testing. Failure to do this can result in incorrect level control.*

Typical single level switch that is fitted to many basic machines.

Some pressure switches may have their tube connections on the rear plate. This is only a variation on the fixing type and does not impair the operation of the switch.

Diagrams illustrate the theoretical operation of a single level pressure switch. A. Being the live supply. Point B. is the empty position of the pressure switch, and in this position power supplied to A via the programme timer would be allowed to flow to the fill valve via B. When the preset level of water is reached, the diaphragm of the pressure switch pushes the contact arm across to contact C. Power to the fill valve is therefore stopped and transferred to connection C. Fig 2, which in turn could supply the circulation motor and heater.

Remember that base mounted pressure switches require the pressure tube to be looped above the normal water level. Failure to do this can cause problems with water levels.

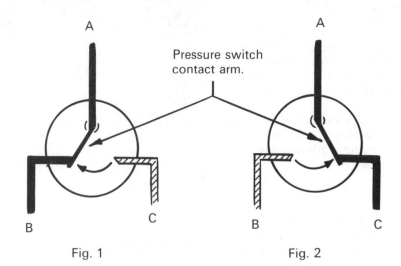

Pressure switch contact arm.

Fig. 1   Fig. 2

Machines with pressure switches fitted below the base of the load compartment (below water level) must then loop the pressure tube above water level height, usually at the side of the cabinet between the outer cover. This will ensure that the water cannot enter the switch even if failure resulting in over filling occurs.

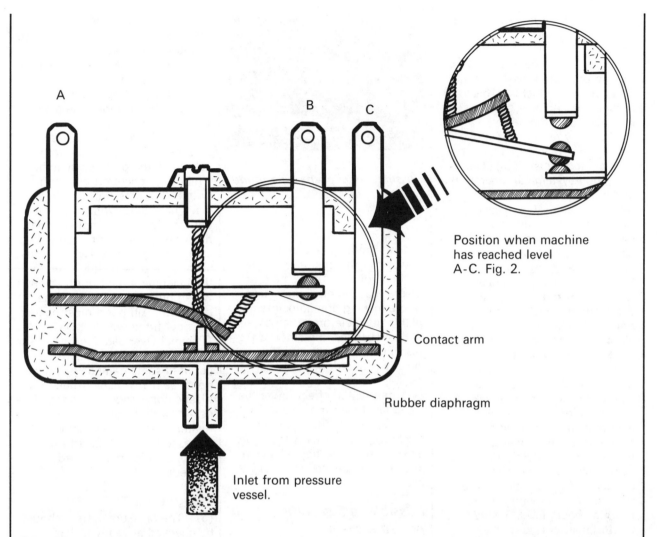

Position when machine
has reached level
A-C. Fig. 2.

Contact arm

Rubber diaphragm

Inlet from pressure
vessel.

Checking a pressure switch

By blowing into the switch via the pressure tube, the audible "clicks" of the switches should be heard. This should also happen when the pressure is released. If your machine uses a single level of water, one click will be heard, two levels of water will produce two clicks. Many machines have an over-fill level detection system which will activate the outlet pump should any excess water enter the machine for any reason. This system may simply be a second switch of the existing pressure switch, operated by the increased pressure of the over-fill. Unfortunately, a system that uses the same pressure vessel for both normal and abnormal water level detection, may fail to detect

over-filling if it is caused by a blocked pressure vessel or hose. A system using a separate pressure vessel and a separate pressure switch for detecting over-filling are much less prone to failure of this nature. Nevertheless, they still require cleaning and checking frequently.

On many dishwashers, a bleed tube is fitted below the pressure vessel and connected to the outlet pump or branch of the sump hose or to the sump chamber. This ensures that, as the water level in the machine drops, the level in the pressure vessel is not then held by a semi-vacuum in the vessel top. Such retention of water would give a false level on the next fill. When checking or overhauling the pressure system, make sure that all such hoses are completely clear of

sediments, fat deposits, etc.
(a)   When the diaphragm becomes "holed" or porous. The switch can be operated and clicks heard, but will click back again without being de-pressurised.
(b)   The contact points inside the switch may "weld" themselves together. This will alter the number of clicks heard, as one or more may be inoperative. Movement of the switch can free the points, although this will not be a lasting repair, as the switch will fail again.

Any of the above faults require the fitting of a new switch. The make, model and serial number of the machine should be stated when ordering, as pressure switches are internally pre-set for specific machines, although the external appearance is similar. Fitting is a simple direct exchange between the old and new.

Some machines may have a second pressure vessel with a pressure tube attached. This second pressure vessel comes into operation should the water level for any reason rise above normal, (i.e. failure of valve on normal pressure system). This anti-flood system can operate the outlet pump via a second pressure switch, (i.e. discharge the water constantly until over-filling has ceased), or operate a special pressure operated valve situated between the inlet valve and air break. This later system shuts off the internal water supply mechanically and not electrically. Such valves may also incorporate a mechanical float flood protection system. This system uses a recess in the base plate of the machine to catch any spilt water or leak. Any accumulation of water will allow a large float to be lifted and shut off the mechanical valve. This type of flood protection is more commonly found on built-in machines. Correct operation of such systems depend on the machine being level. Ensure that the installation is correct and check regularly.

Arrowed is a sump hose mounted pressure vessel – early Indesit type prone to fat blockages.

On some dishwashers, the level of water can be adjusted simply by raising or lowering the pressure vessel or float chamber as the case may be. The reason this can be done is that the

Pressure vessel of the type found on various makes.

systems are actuated by the level of water in the machine and not its total volume. Take care and ensure that the machine is level before making any adjustments. With adjustable pressure vessels or float systems, the amount the vessel is raised or lowered is directly proportional to water level, i.e., a lowering of the vessel by 1 mm will in effect lower the water level by 1 mm. Note: Do not make any adjustments to level switch systems without first making sure that they are clean and clear of any sediment or blockages.

Possible faults in the pressure system

To create the highest pressure in the chamber of the pressure vessel, the vessel must be positioned as low as possible in the machine. Any sediment that is in the machine collects at this point and can therefore block the entrance. Similarly, because of its very small internal diameter, the pressure tube can also block easily. The pressure that this device creates is very small, and can easily be blocked by a very small obstruction, such as a lump of powder or sediment deposits.

The seals and hoses of the system are also of great importance. These should be checked for air leaks and blockages. Any puncture or blockage would create a loss of pressure, resulting in the incorrect operation of the switches, i.e., if

the air pressure in the pressure vessel were to leak out, the vessel would fill with water. Thinking that the machine was now empty, the water valves would be re-energised, thus filling an already full machine. The results would be obvious.

The above example assumed that the air was stopped from getting to the pressure switch. If a blockage occurred whilst the switch was pressurised, the machine would work as normal until the machine emptied. The next time a programme was started the pressure switch would already be pressurised. Therefore the machine would not take any water, but proceed to turn the heater on. Although most heaters are now fitted with a T.O.C. (Thermal Overload Cutout) – (see *Glossary of terms*), this may not act until some damage has been done, as many dishwashers have plastic components or liners. It is essential that the T.O.C. or heater over-heat protector is not bypassed and if found to be faulty, should be renewed immediately.

Points to note.
(a)   The pressure system should be checked at yearly or half yearly intervals, depending on the water hardness in your area, (more often if large amounts of fatty foods are washed off in the water).
(b)   Dishwasher pressure systems are often affected regardless of water conditions. Fat deposits can block the pressure vessel, allowing the water level to rise to a leakage point.
(c)   Any hoses or tubes that have been removed must be sealed, and any clips tightened.
(d)   Blowing down the accessible end of the pressure tube may seem an easy solution to remove a blockage, but this may only be a temporary cure. Also, water may enter the pressure vessel before you can push the end of the tube back onto the pressure switch. This

will render the pressure system inaccurate, if not useless.

(e)   When tilting or laying the machine over for repair or servicing, ensure that water droplets do not lodge within the pressure tube as they will cause incorrect operaton of the pressure system.

(f)   The water level in some machines can be adjusted slightly by raising or lowering the pressure vessel. Early Candy machines are an example of this and certain other makes have similar adjustments. All such adjustments are limited.

(g)   A pressure switch should only be suspected when the system has been thoroughly cleaned, checked, sealed and re-tested.

Dynamic Performance Control D.P.C. – what is it?

Some machines may be fitted with an extra hose connection on the main circulation pump chamber. This will be connected directly to a separate pressure switch and secured firmly with much larger clips than normally seen on pressure systems. This is no ordinary pressure switch – it is a "high pressure" switch and cannot be tested by blowing into it and listening for the switch to 'make'. The pressure to operate this switch is in excess of 25 times that of a normal level switch. Its purpose is to monitor the main pump pressure. If the pump 'hunts' and pressure drops in the chamber, the switch which is normally held open circuit, will close. This system is called D.P.C. – Dynamic Performance Control.

How does it work?

D.P.C. quite simply means that if dynamic performance of the pump, (the energy transferred to the water), drops below the preset limit, it is probably due to lack of water getting to the pump from the sump. This may be caused by poor cleaning of filter,

over foaming or most likely an item in the wash load incorrectly stacked which has filled with water therefore reducing the overall water level for the wash. On most machines this would lead to a poor wash result due to lack of water to spray arms, etc. D.P.C. counteracts this by sensing the drop in pump pressure and compensates by allowing extra water in until the pressure is high enough to operate the D.P.C. pressure switch thus stopping the water inlet. You may think flooding would occur due to over-filling, but a normal over-fill switch is fitted in the same circuit to prevent this happening.

The system appears to work well and in reality adds very little complexity to the machine.

Venturi systems

Some machines will have, in addition to the normal type of pressure system, a float device situated in the sump or centre section of the machine's base. This float device is not used for accidental over-fill situations. Its purpose is to allow the machine to fill higher than the level governed by the pre-set switch. This is necesssary to avoid

unwanted tripping of the water softener valve which would occur when the main wash/circulation pump starts, thus reducing the water level by its operation. The higher level is achieved by a venturi effect of passing water past the pressure vessel base opening, thus causing a pressure drop within the chamber. The float is designed to float at the higher level and in so doing, it shuts off the flow through its base. This action then allows the level to rise quickly around the float chamber and for the level to equalise in the fill tube and load compartment. The slowing and eventual stopping of the flow past the pressure vessel base cancels the venturi effect and pressure returns to operate the switch with a slightly higher pressure than is actually required. In simple terms – if the pressure switch was used only to govern the water level, the following sequence would occur. When the pre-set level is reached and the main circulation pumps starts, the water level will reduce so quickly that the pressure switch will sense the drop and re-energise the fill valve. If such a float and venturi system were not employed, the valve, pressure switch and motor would 'trip' several times.

Air vent

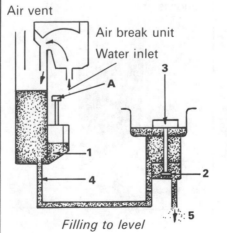

Air break unit
Water inlet

Filling to level

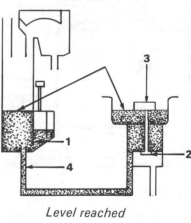

Level reached

Venturi float system operation

Venturi float operation

As water flows along pipe 4 and through outlet 5 to the lowest part of the machine, a pressure drop in vessel 1 is created. This is maintained until the float 3 shuts off valve 2. With the flow now stopped along 4, the venturi effect is stopped and pressure is built up in vessel 1. This pressure is higher than would normally be created by this pressure vessel. Gravity then levels the water in both inlet and load compartment. The higher level alleviates the problem caused when the main circulation pump starts to operate and reduces the overall level slightly.

Simple float operation

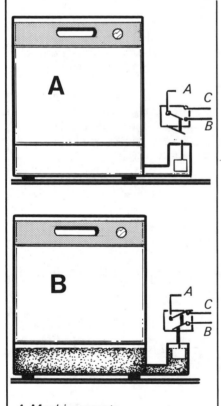

A Machine empty.

B Machine at correct water level.

This simplified drawing shows the float switch operation.

Like the illustration on pressure switches, A is the 'live' supply and B the empty position allowing in this instance a supply to the fill valve. When water level is reached B the float rises and pushes the microswitch contact arm to the C position. This removes the power supply to the valve (stopping filling) and allows power to flow through contact C to the circulation motor in this instance.

This is a simplified float system operation. The location of the float and microswitches will vary between makes and models. The float system is in many cases combined with the air break and steam vent mouldings situated between the inner and outer side panels. As with the pressure system, check for blockages and fat deposits. The microswitches can be easily tested. See *Electrical circuit testing (Using a meter)*.

Float switch operation is quite simply what it says – as the water rises, a float is lifted and at the correct level actuates a microswitch with this action. The placing of both pressure vessels and float systems varies and can sometimes be an integral part of a complicated plastic moulding of both water inlet, air vent, steam vent and level systems. Due to their complex moulding, it is important that they are clean and free from blockages and fat deposits etc.

Always isolate machine completely before any repair.

Pressure system stripdown

This particular machine had only one pressure vessel and switch. Machines with additional pressure vessels and switches would require all hoses etc., checking. Some modern machines have the hose and vessel situated to cause a degree of self cleaning to take place when emptying which is designed to reduce deposit build-up.
Check and adjust level of the machine before functional test for water level.

Carefully lay machine over if necessary, to gain access to pressure system hoses. In this instance the side panel had to be removed.

Both pressure vessel and hose were thought to be blocked.

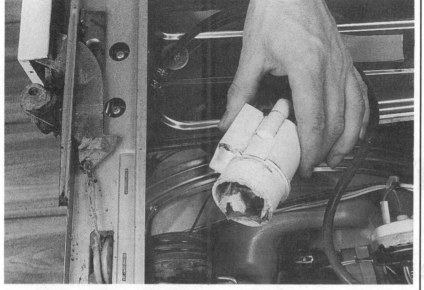

In this case, a build-up of fatty deposits has collected in both vessel and hose. Thorough cleaning was required.

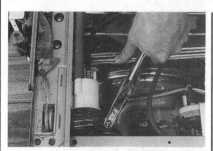

Remove clips and connections to pressure vessel.

Seal and re-fit all hoses and panels securely.

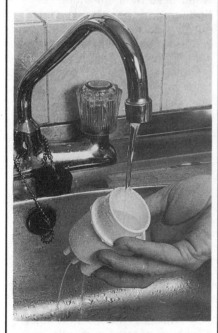

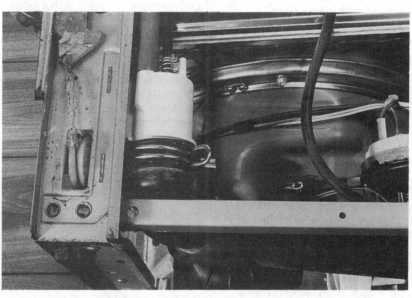

Clean the vessel and hoses thoroughly prior to re-assembly.

Chapter 21

Internal water softeners

What is a water softener?

A water softener is a means of removing excessive levels of calcium and magnesium in suspension within the ordinary domestic supply. Such levels vary considerably from region to region but your local Water Authority will advise you regarding the levels in your particular area.

Why have a water softener in the machine?

The reason why most dishwashers are fitted with water softeners is because of the way they wash and dry the load. The chemicals used for cleaning, combined with the water containing high levels of calcium and magnesium, would cause scale build up on the wash load, resulting in a rough, dull, opaque layer on crockery, glassware, etc. See: *Common causes of poor washing results.*

Do you really need a softener?

A water softener is necessary if your water supply is 15 H.F. (hardness factor), or above. If a large domestic softener has previously been installed for all your household use, you need not fill the regeneration compartment in your dishwasher with salt, as further softening is not necessary. This may also apply for hardness factors of below 15. The machine will still fill via the softener device and no action to your machine needs to be taken to modify the machine in either case.

If you own a machine that does not have a water softener unit fitted, (not all machines have them as standard fittings), and you are encountering the build up of a dull rough layer on crockery, glass, etc., check the hardness factor for your area. If the result is above 15 H.F. it could be worth finding out from the manufacturer of your machine if a softener kit can be obtained for your dishwasher. The lack of a salt compartment top within the base of the load compartment will confirm if a softener unit is not fitted to your machine.

How does a water softener work?

The water softener unit is made up of two linked compartments, one sealed and containing resin granules, and the other compartment is a fillable container for salt. Most dishwashers use softened water for the wash and end rinse cycles only, whilst others soften all the water used by the machine. Softening of the water is carried out by passing the in-coming water through the resin beads in compartment B. The resin granules are designed to attract calcium ions $(Ca++)$ and magnesium ions $(Mg++)$. They do this by in turn releasing sodium ions $(Na+)$. The emerging water is therefore softened by the removal of both calcium and magnesium by the loss from the resin of sodium. After passing through such a softener, water with a hardness factor of 40 H.F. will now be in the region of 7 – 10 H.F. For the resin to work efficiently as a softener, it must be replenished with sodium ions. This operation is called regeneration.

With use, the resin granules become saturated with calcium and magnesium ions and possess few sodium ions. Regeneration is done by simply passing salt water (water containing sodium $(Na+)$ through the resin, therefore allowing the resin to absorb a fresh supply of sodium (Na+), so becoming regenerated and ready for use. To allow an optimum interchange of sodium ions on the regeneration cycle the water flow is restricted, i.e., slowed down to around 1 litre per minute, to allow a thorough regeneration and interchange to take place.

Regeneration is done automatically by the machine at the beginning or end of the cycle depending on the make and model. The frequency of regeneration is governed by a small knob on the switch that is set to correspond to the hardness of the water in your area. (Not all machines have this facility). The time taken to regenerate can be twenty minutes or more, allowing time for the transfer of sodium ions back into the resin. It is,

therefore unwise to restart the machine unless twenty minutes or more have elapsed, particularly if the indicator is set for a hard water area. The water used for regeneration is pumped away by the outlet pump during the generation cycle. NB. Machines that regenerate at the beginning of every cycle take much less time than those that regenerate only after several wash cycles have been completed. The amount of cycles between regeneration is governed by the hardness of selector i.e. soft water selected – more cycles between regeneration. With machines that regenerate at the beginning of every cycle, the regeneration is usually governed by passing a fixed volume of water through the system. The volume increases with higher

settings of the hardness selector. This can be done on a timed basis or by a mechanical system which is combined into the airbreak unit. Three compartments of varying sizes within the airbreak fill whenever the machine operates and it is a combination of these that governs the strength of regeneration, i.e. 1 compartment – soft, 3 compartments – hard. Water is allowed to flow slowly, under gravity only, through the softener unit during the regeneration cycle.

The water softener will require regular filling with salt as per the instruction manual. On average, compartment A will take approximately 2.2 kilogrammes of salt which under normal conditions is enough for between six and seven regenerations. The

WATER HARDNESS COMPARISON CHART

Length of Regeneration	Hardness	Parts per million P.P.M.	Mg/L CACO₃	Grains per British Gal. (Clarke) degrees	German degrees	French degrees	Grains per U.S. Gal.
NO SALT REQUIRED	S	0	0	0	0	0	0
		25	25.17	1.75	1.41	2.52	1.5
	MS	50	50.33	3.5	2.82	5.03	3
		100	100.66	7	5.64	10.07	5.8
	SH	120	122.23	8.5	6.84	12.22	7.0
		150	150.99	10.5	8.45	15.10	8.7
	MH	200	201.32	14	11.27	20.13	11.7
NORMAL REGENERA-TION	H	260	258.84	18	14.49	25.88	15
		300	301.98	21	16.91	30.20	17.5
	VH	350	352.31	24.5	19.73	35.23	20.4
		400	402.64	28	22.54	40.26	23.3
LONG REGENERA-TION		430	431.40	30	24.15	43.14	25

amount of salt consumption of a dishwasher is sometimes overlooked or ignored altogether, but such oversights can cause problems with the quality of the wash. Check regularly and top up the salt compartment to maintain optimum efficiency of this unit. The salt used for regeneration can be anti-calcium salt or unrefined cooking salt; but better still are the packs of salt in granular form sold especially for dishwashers. DO NOT USE TABLE SALT as it may have additives such as iodine which can cause problems to your machine.

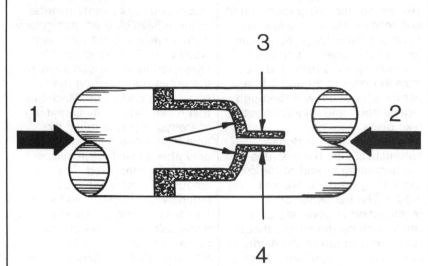

Water hardness

The degree of hardness can be expressed in various ways and each country seems to have a different way of expressing the hardness factor. The handbook for your dishwasher may give the factor in figures applicable to the country in which it was manufactured. The table shown will help in assessing correctly your particular water hardness factor which may be expressed on a different scale.

Water can be supplied to the softener unit at point (I) for normal filling and softening. The

water is forced to pass through the resin and out at point (H). Flow through the salt compartment cannot occur due to the non-return valve. Regeneration of the resin is done by supplying water to the unit via (E). Water flows slowly first through the salt and dissolves a little as it does. The water with the salt in suspension then passes through the resin and out at point (H) regenerating the resin granules as it does so. The non-return valve (F2) prevents water escaping at point (I).

The non-return valve with the softener unit

The non-return valves within the softener unit are simply a shaped rubber seal (See diagram). Water entering at point (I) will push open the valve. If a back pressure or reverse feed occurs (2), the resulting pressure at point 3 and 4 effectively closes the valve tightly shut.

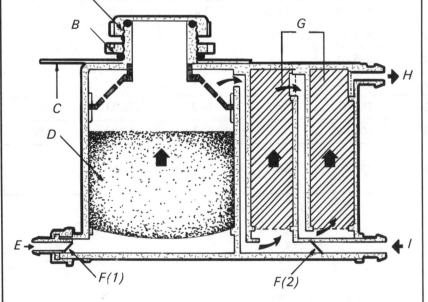

The softener unit

A. Salt container top (may contain float indicator).
B. Retaining nut and rubber seal.
C. Load compartment base.
D. Salt.
E. Regeneration water inlet.

F1&2 Non-return valves.
G. Resin granules.
H. Outlet to load compartment for both softened and regenerated water.
I. Main inlet for water to be softened prior to use in machine.

A complete water softener unit from a Hoover dishwasher showing clearly the two containers: left – the salt reservoir and right – the resin container, and various pipe connectors.

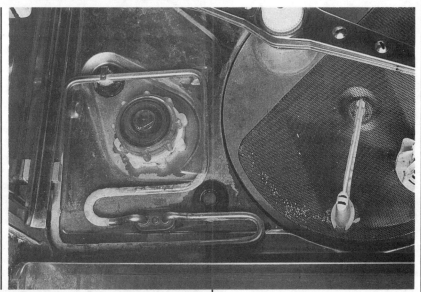

All that is normally seen of the softener system. Check regularly that the salt indicator is working.

Softener unit viewed from underside of the load cabinet.

Area guide to water hardness in the UK

Due to a new grid system for water, hardness may vary considerably in times of shortage. Details shown are therefore only an indication of normally expected hardness.

	Parts per million as $CaCO_3$	Degrees Clark	Degrees French
Soft	0–50	0–3.5	8–5
Moderately soft	50–100	3.5–7.0	5–10
Slightly hard	100–150	7.0–10.5	10–15
Moderately hard	150–200	10.5–14.0	15–20
Hard	200–300	14.0–21.0	20–30
Very hard	over 300	over 21.0	over 30

Area	Authority	Water Hardness	Area	Authority	Water Hardness
Argyll	Scotland	S	London – Metropolitan	Thames	MH – VH
Ashborne	Severn – Trent	MS – H	Lune Valley	North West	S – SH
Avon and Dorset	Wessex	H	Macclesfield	North West	MS – H
Ayrshire	Scotland	S	Makerfield	North West	S – MH
Birmingham	Severn – Trent	S – VH	Manchester	North West	S
Bolton	North West	S	Mersey Valley	North West	S – VH
Bournemouth	Wessex	H – VH	Montgomery	Severn – Trent	S – MH
Cambridge	Anglia	SH – H	Newcastle & Gateshead	Northumbrian	MH
Carlisle	North West	MS	Nottingham	Severn – Trent	MS – MH
Cheshire – Mid	North West	MS – H	Northumberland &		
Chester	North West	SH – H	Tyne	Northumbrian	SH
Chiltern	Thames	VH	Nuneaton	Severn – Trent	SH – VH
Clyde – Lower	Scotland	S	Pennine – West	North West	S – MS
Colna Valley	North West	H – VH	Plymouth	South West	S – SH
Corby & District	North West	H	Preston & District	North West	S
Cumbria South	North West	S – MH	Rickmansworth &		
Cumbria West	North West	S	Uxbridge Valley	Thames	H – VH
Derbyshire – North	Severn – Trent	S – H	Salop	Severn – Trent	H
Derbyshire – South	Severn – Trent	MH	Scilly Isles	–	MH
Derwent Valley	Severn – Trent	S	Scotland – Mid	Scotland	S – MH
East Anglia	Anglia	H – VH	Scotland – North	Scotland	S – VH
Eastbourne	Southern	SH – VH	Scotland – North East	Scotland	S
Eden	North West	S – MH	Scotland – South East	Scotland	S – H
Essex	Anglia	S – VH	Scotland – South West	Scotland	S – MH
Exeter	South West	S – H	Sherwood	Severn – Trent	MH – VH
Fife & Kinross	Scotland	S – VH	Somerset	Wessex	S – VH
Folkestone & District	Southern	S – VH	Stafford	Severn – Trent	H – VH
Fylde	North West	S – SH	Staffordshire – South	Severn – Trent	H – VH
Gloucester	Severn – Trent &		St. Helens	North West	SH
	Thames	MH – VH	Stockport	North West	S
Guernsey	–	SH	Sunderland & South Shields	Northumbrian	MS – VH
Hampshire Central	Southern	H	Surrey East	Thames	MS
Hampshire North	Southern	H	Surrey North	Thames	H – VH
Hampshire West	Southern	H	Sussex	Southern	H
Hartlepool	Northumbrian	H – VH	Sussex East	Southern	MS
Invernesshire	Scotland	S – MH	Sussex Mid	Southern	S – H
Ireland Eastern	–	S – H	Sussex North West	Southern	MS – VH
Ireland Northern	–	MS	Sutton District	Thames	SH
Ireland Southern	–	S – VH	Tees	Northumbrian	S – MS
Ireland Western	–	MS	Tendring Hundred	Anglia	H
Isle of Wight	–	SH – H	Truro	South West	S – SH
Jersey	–	MH	Vales	Thames	MS – VH
Kent	Southern	H	Warwickshire	Severn – Trent	MH – VH
Kent East	Southern	H	Wear	Northumbrian	S
Kent Mid	Southern	SH – VH	Wiltshire	Thames	H
Kent West	Southern	MS – H	Wolverhampton	Severn – Trent	SH – VH
Lakes & Lune	North West	S	Worcestershire –		
Lambourne	Thames	SH – VH	North	Severn – Trent	S – VH
Lanarkshire	North West	S – VH	Worcestershire –		
Lancashire	North West	S – VH	South	Severn – Trent	MS – H
Lee Valley	Thames	VH	Wrexham & East		
Leicester	Severn – Trent	MH – VH	Wrexham Denbighshire	Welsh	SH
Liverpool	North West	S – SH	York	Yorkshire	H
Loch Lomond	Scotland	S	Yorkshire North	Yorkshire	S – VH
Loch Turret	Scotland	S			

Chapter 22

Heater

Where is the heater located?

The heater is located on the lower part of the load compartment or inside the sump well of the machine. Size and shape of heaters vary enormously from manufacturer to manufacturer. Some are used only when immersed in water whilst others operate immersed for wash cycles and for a very short period when uncovered to help dry the load at the end of the cycle.

Removal and refitting of the heater

To remove the heater:
Make a note of the connections and remove them, the heater can then be withdrawn from its position by removing the centre nut, and fixing plate. Next lift the heater free from any retaining clips inside the load compartment.

Refitting is a reversal of these instructions, ensuring that all securing clips are refitted and good contact is made with overheat thermostats, etc. Care should be taken that the centre nut is not overtightened, as this would cause a distortion of the metal plate.

Main faults with heaters

One of the most common faults with the heater is that of open circuit, i.e. No current flows through the heater, therefore no heat is produced, and the machine will fail to move off the wash programme as the impulse via the thermostat will not be produced. This can be due to a broken or loose connection to one of the heater terminals. This then overheats, leaving an obvious discoloration of the connection or terminal, resulting in a break of the circuit at that point. Alternatively, the break in the circuit can occur within the element itself. This can be tested for continuity, as described in the section: Using your meter.

Another fault that can occur is that of low insulation. In this case please refer to Chapter 29. *Low insulation.* Accompanying the low insulation fault is that of the short circuiting of the heater, caused by a complete breakdown of insulation. This results in the machine blowing fuses or earth tripping.

Should any of the above faults occur, a complete replacement of the component is required. This is so, even for the double element heaters. If one of the two elements should fail, a complete element replacement is needed.

Many machines have plastic or nylon load compartments and are fitted with overheat protectors. These are essential and are linked in line with the live feed to the heater. They are fitted for safety reasons, for if a pressure switch or pressure system were to fail, it is possible for the heater to be engaged with no water in the machine.

In a machine with a metal load compartment, this would be most unwelcome, but only minor damage would be caused. If this were to happen in a machine with a plastic/nylon compartment, the result could be extremely dangerous. Note: Under no circumstances should the overheat protection be removed or bypassed.

The overheat protector that is used on some Philips machines is an integral part of the heater and is similar to a capillary thermostat switch. It can be reset by pressing the reset button on the unit. A protector which is found to be open circuit or tripped, would result in no heating of the wash water and would also cause the machine to 'stop' i.e. fail to move through the programme. If this item is found to be 'open circuit', check the pressure switch and system prior to renewing the overheat device.

Another problem that can affect the heater and its safety cut-out is scale build-up or a covering of food sediment. This can cause the heater to be in effect, insulated from the water surrounding it and unable to transfer its heat quickly enough to the water. Such overheating of the element causes the safety cut-out to operate. In this instance, a thorough cleaning of the element would be required and a check on why the build-up had occurred, (possibly lack of filter cleaning, under-dosing of powder, failure of softener system, etc.). A similar fault is caused by too little water for circulation, exposing the element during main circulation motor operations. Check levels and listen for the pump 'hunting' during the wash as the pump will, for a second, run out of water to circulate.

Incorrect or poor quality powders can also cause 'hunting' and premature heater failure due to excessive foaming.

A new style of heater is now appearing in some modern machines. There is no visible evidence of a heater in the load compartment or sump unit. It is mounted in line with the sump unit or hose, and links directly to the circulation pump inlet. The heater element is externally wound around a stainless steel tube and transfers heat to the water via this tube. The users of this type of heater state that it cannot fur or scale up in any way and technically they are correct as the heater does not come directly into contact with the water. However, scale can and does form in the tube in certain circumstances, (i.e. not using salt etc.). Also, being in line with the pump inlet, the water flowing through the heat tube is drawn through the filter giving rise to problems if the filter is not cleaned regularly and thoroughly. The heater unit is fitted with a T.O.C. but often it is not a self-setting one. If the T.O.C. has tripped, make sure of the reason for it having done so and rectify the problem prior to resetting, i.e. clean filters thoroughly or, in the case of scaling, remove the unit and clean thoroughly. (Take care if using descaling chemicals and follow the manufacturers' instructions for use). Identify also the reason why the unit scaled up in the first place and rectify the problem. **As with any repairs – ensure the machine is isolated before removing any panels. Taps off and plug out.**

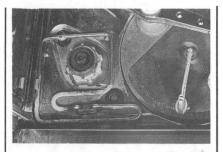
Base mounted heater.

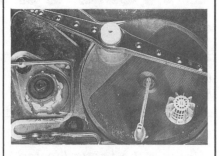
Overheat thermostat position on heater (self-setting version).

Badly scaled element caused by hard water area and infrequent salt container filling.

Normal condition of element after use. Pictured here with overheat thermostat fitted.

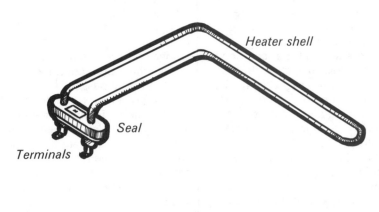
The heater

Chapter 23

Thermostats

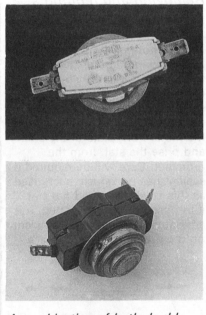

Single thermostat

Double thermostat.

A combination of both double and single thermostats is most often found giving three temperature ranges.

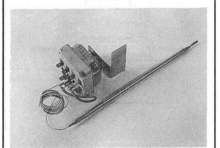

Pod type thermostat found on some dishwashers. This type can have a greater range of temperatures from just the one probe.

What is a thermostat?

A thermostat is an automatic instrument for regulating temperature. In the case of dishwashers this can be water temperature or the direct heat of the heating element (in which case, acting like a T.O.C. See Chapter 22, *Heater*). The thermostat (stat.) will also either 'make' or 'break' a circuit at a pre-determined temperature. Temperature ratings are usually marked around the metal perimeter on the back of the stat. and also marked NO or NC, i.e. normally open contact – closing and making a circuit at given temperature, or normally closed – opening at given temperature. Some thermostats can and do contain both variants.

Where is it located?

The thermostat is located under the bottom panel or base of the dishwasher in contact with the metal base or with a grommet fitted through it to come into direct contact with the water or heater. Access to it is by laying the machine over on its back.

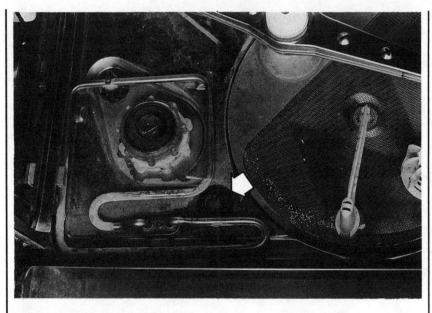

Base of load compartment of this Candy machine shows the position of grommet fitted double thermostat (arrowed).

for closing or opening of the thermostat can now be carried out as shown in the section: Electrical fault finding (*Using a meter.*)

Check temperature with a household thermometer and allow a few degrees either way of the marked temperature on the outer rim of the stat, and remember to check if the stat. is normally NO or NC. When cool, check that the stat returns to its normal position as indicated on the rim, i.e. NO or NC.

Most thermostats are grommet fitted, i.e. fitted into a rubber seal and then in turn fitted to a hole in the machine's base. Always ensure a watertight fit. The use of a little sealant is advisable to assist stat fitting to grommets. See *Useful tips and information.* Thermostats may also be held in position by metal clips or clamps, and again, make sure of a good seal and check that the clips or clamps do not trap or touch wires or connectors.

How does it work?

Diagrams show a typical thermostat, in this instance a 50°C (NO) normally open contact and a 85°C (NC) normally closed contact. The latter is a safety thermostat which operates if overheating should occur within the machine. Normal operational temperatures of dishwashers are much lower with a maximum rating rarely exceeding 65°C.

The diagram illustrates the position of a thermostat at rest. Bi-metal discs are mounted directly behind the metal front cover of the stat and are preset to distort at given temperature (in this instance 50°C and 85°C). They are linked to contact switches by push rods. Any corresponding distortions of the

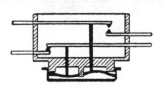

AT REST POSITION

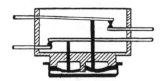

50° TEMP REACHED

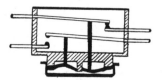

OVERHEAT
SUPPLY TO HEATER DIRECT
CUT OFF

discs, either make or break the corresponding contacts as shown.

When removed from the machine, the thermostat's operation can be tested by placing the metal cover in contact with a known heat source, i.e. radiator, hot water, etc., which matches or slightly exceeds the required temperature. Allow a little time for the heat to warm the stat and bimetal discs. Testing

Removing and refitting a grommet thermostat

Make a note of the position, orientation and connections of the thermostat and then disconnect the wires. Insert a small flat bladed screwdriver between the inner rubber lip and the metal front plate of the stat. and prise the stat. from the grommet. Care will be required if sealant has previously been used as this will have glued the stat. into position. When refitting, it is advisable to smear a little sealant on the grommet to avoid leaks.

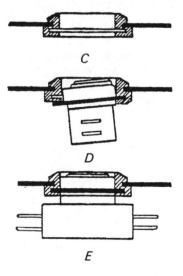

C

D

E

THERMOSTAT FITTING

Refitting is a reversal of the removal process. See Diagrams C. D. E.

To refit
Locate the metal lip in grommet recess (D) and with the aid of a flat bladed screwdriver ease the outer lip over the metal lip of the stat (C). Sealant will help locate and seal the thermostat into position. (E) Ensure that the thermostat is securely located in to the grommet and that the outer lip is not trapped.

WARNING: Before attempting to remove or repair any component from the machine, isolate the machine from the main electrical supply by removing the plug from the wall socket.

Thermostat operation flowchart

Using the following flowchart, trace the sequence of events:

1   The machine is turned on.
2   The timer impulses, fills the machine with cold water and turns the heater on.
3 – 4   The thermostat 'waits' until the heater has heated the water to 40°C.
5 – 6   When the thermostat closes (i.e. the water has reached 40°C), the timer washes for two minutes. The timer starts the washing action for two minutes. (At this point the heater is still engaged).
7 – 8   The above operation is repeated, again with the heater engaged. When the two minute wash has ended, the water will be at 45°C due to the extra four minute heating.
9 – 11 The timer then moves to the next position, which disengages the heater, and would then be ready for the programme to continue as required.
12 For the purpose of this flowchart, the wash will end here as we are only concerned with the operation of the thermostat at this time.

Note: This is only used as an example to illustrate the use of the thermostat, and does not actually represent the way in which a wash is formed. For further information regarding the timer, see Chapter 28: *Timers (programmers)*.
   This way of using preset thermostats can give a greater variation in wash temperatures.

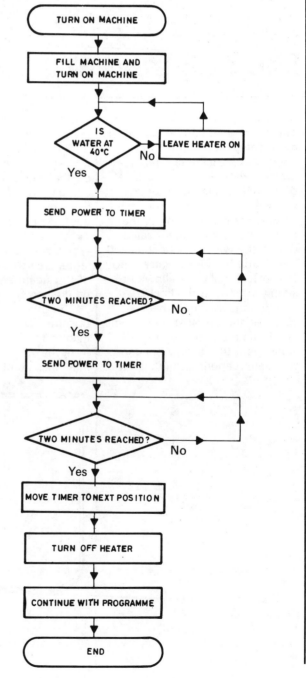

Chapter 24

The steam vent

The steam vent can be part of the more complex moulding of combined pressure system, float system, water inlet and air break or a much smaller unit for steam venting only. Whether combined or separate the function of the unit is the same. Water heated during the wash and final heated rinse naturally forms water vapour (steam). If this were allowed to simply vent in to the kitchen, it would condense on other surfaces and be most unwelcome. To alleviate this problem, the steam vent unit simply condenses the water vapour and returns it to the sump to be pumped away during the empty cycle.

The unit is usually mounted on the side of the load compartment between the inner and outer cover. Only the small inlet (A) is visible. This leads directly into compartment (B) which is much larger. It is this larger area that condenses most of the steam back into water to be drained by outlet (C).

In this picture the extra position (D) is in fact the water inlet to the load compartment from the softener unit. Many machines combine inlet and steam vent to cut down on entry points into the load area.

In most cases, it is necessary to remove the side panel to gain access to the main body of the unit. As with all repairs, isolate the machine prior to any repair or adjustment: plug out and taps off.

Problems with vent systems are usually rare and are mainly caused by blockages or cracking of the moulded unit. When the steam vent is combined with inlet or other systems, ensure all hoses are noted prior to removal and refit all hoses, clips and seals securely.

A   B   C

Chapter 25

Detergent dispensers

For dishwashers to work correctly the powder (or new liquid) detergents must be added at the correct point of the wash programme. If it is added too early it will be flushed away on the pre-rinse, too late and it will not have sufficient time to act on the wash load.

The way in which the detergent is added (dispensed) is by means of a closable container which will open at a predetermined point in the wash cycle, the contents of which will be flushed out by the spray action. This achieves a quick and thorough mixing of the detergent and water at the correct time of the wash programme.

Three versions of dispensers are commonly found – the simplest being a small drawer type container in which the detergent is placed and flushed into the load compartment during filling for main wash. The other two versions each have a spring loaded cover or slide that is manually latched shut by the user and unlatched by the machine by means of:

A. A purely mechanical operation linked directly to the timer cam. At a set point the cam pushes a connecting arm and unlatches the dispenser cover (this type often controls rinse aid dispensing in the same way but at a different point in the programme).

B. Electro-mechanical operation of the dispenser cover. Two further variations of electrically-operated dispensers can be found – 1. A small heater wound around a bimetal strip. When energised, the bending of the bimetal strip unlatches the dispenser cover. 2. A solenoid and magnet latch system. When closed a permanent magnet holds the cover in position, when power is supplied to the solenoid coil, the magnetism induced in the coil cancels the permanent magnet's field and therefore it can no longer hold the latch in position and the dispenser cover opens.

Care must be taken with all dispensers as they are easily jammed or strained. When loading with detergent, try to keep the load central and not foul the catch or slide.

The most common problems are sticking shut or breaking of the cover, (especially on flap dispensers). Some manufacturers will supply new covers, but other faults such as open circuit of coils or heaters will require the renewal of the whole unit. This is

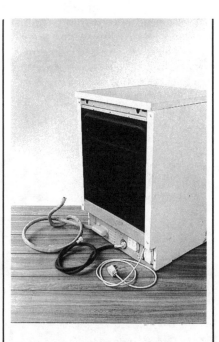

As always, before any repair completely isolate the machine.

a simple task which necessitates the removal of the outer door cover which will give access to the dispenser unit and its fixing screws. As with any repair or service isolate the machine completely before starting.

Machines with mechanically linked timer and dispenser will need to be reset if either the timer has been removed or incorrect dispensing is suspected. Most work on a tappet type action similar to that of a car engine. Correct operation depends on a tappet clearance of between 1 and 2 mm, usually attained by an adjusting screw. This operation can be checked by turning the timer manually and observing the movement at the correct part of the cam cycle. As before, all adjustments and work should be done with the machine completely isolated – not just switched off but with plug pulled out!

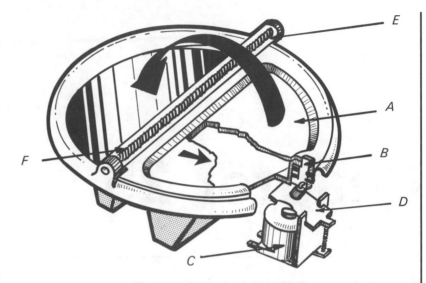

Electro-mechanical dispenser

The illustration shows one of the many variations of powder dispensers used in dishwashers. This is a latch operated unit. The dispenser is filled with the correct amount of detergent and cover 'A' is closed and held in position by latch 'B'. At the correct point

of the programme, solenoid 'C' is energized and in this instance attracts plate 'D' by electromagnetism. This movement is transferred to latch 'B' and

releases the latch. Return spring 'E' and hinge 'F' flips cover 'A' open and exposes the detergent to the wash water to be dispersed by the wash action.

This dispenser is similar to the diagram but has a sliding compartment cover and latching is by a magnet. When the solenoid is energized, the permanent magnet latch is cancelled out and the return spring slides the compartment open.

This Candy dispenser is one of the most simple. At the correct part of the cycle, water is flushed through the unit, effectively mixing and dispensing the powder or liquid. It dispenses liquid detergent as easily as powders. With no moving parts this unit is easy to maintain. The removable drawer also acts as the measuring cup for detergent usage. More modern Candy machines now use the combined detergent and rinse aid unit which is housed in the door.

Counter weight the door prior to removing the front panel. This prevents the door closing when panel is removed.

Remove the lower outer fixing screws only.

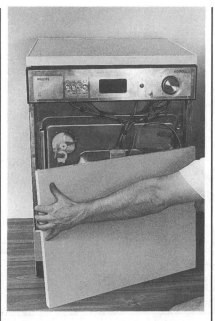

Carefully remove the outer panel. This gives excellent access to the dispenser fixing screws and connections.

Note and remove the connections to the solenoid.

Note the position of the unit and remove the fixing screws.

The unit can now be removed and repaired or replaced. In this instance a new unit complete with seal was required as separate parts were not available. Refitting is a simple reversal of the removal procedure, but do not over-tighten any of the self-tapping screws.

Note: Care must be taken when removing panels on any dishwasher as the edges of the metal panels are rarely cleanly finished after pressing or moulding, (only areas the user would normally come into contact with gets correctly deburred and finished). Such edges can be extremely sharp especially on formed stainless steel, so take care not to slip or run fingers along or near the panel edges.

Chapter 26

Rinse aid dispensers

Typical complete rinse aid dispenser.

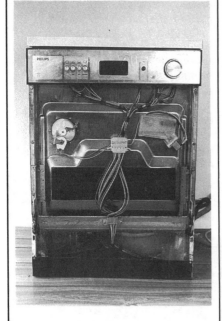

Door assembly inner with rinse aid dispenser in situ.

What is rinse aid?

Rinse aid is essential for the final rinse cycle of all dishwashers. It comes in a concentrated liquid form. Most dishwashers have a reservoir to hold approximately 150 cc of the liquid and at the correct stage in the rinse cycle, it will dispense a pre-determined amount. Rinse aid in this concentrated form is very powerful and care should be exercised when filling the rinse aid reservoir. Avoid contact with skin or eyes, also general spillages. However, in the event of accident splashing or spilling, flush the area with water, but if the liquid has been swallowed, seek medical advice immediately. Remember: Keep all detergents and chemicals out of reach of children.

Normally, only a small amount of rinse aid is required as it is highly diluted as described.

Why use it?

Rinse aid is used in the final rinse to reduce spot marks and streaking when the water evaporates during drying. The drying process is helped greatly by rinse aid leaving the well washed crockery, pots and pans with a clean sparkle.

How does it work?

When mixed with a very large quantity of water the 1–5 cc of concentrate rinse aid reduces the surface tension of the water to stop droplets forming on the wash load. The warm load will then dry more easily as most of the water will have run off the loads' surfaces.

The reduction in water surfaces tension works in a similar way to normal hand washing. Detergent and rinse aid also look very similar, but under no circumstances must the two be confused. Rinse aid is a very concentrated liquid and formulated to be anti-foaming. To use an ordinary liquid detergent would cause foaming and flooding.

If the rinse aid compartment or valve fails and allows excess rinse aid into the machine or weeps rinse aid into the wash cycle, over foaming will occur. Look for the tell tale runs from the discharge point and ensure that the cap is refitted correctly and securely after each fill. Once filled, the rinse aid compartment will not require filling again for sometime and does not need topping up for every wash. If continous filling proves necessary, the unit should then be checked. See: Photo sequence.

Most rinse aid compartments have a system to indicate when topping up is necessary. Some machines have an electrical indicator which is simply a neon light which is activated by the timer after a given number of washes. The most common system is the visual system of which there are two versions. One version is a simple extension of the filler cap which acts like a car dip stick. Simply unscrewing the filler cap and checking if the probe is in contact with the liquid will indicate if topping up is required. The second version has a sight glass that changes colour as the level of rinse aid drops. The indicator can be a separate sight glass or again, part of the filler cap. See: Chart.

FULL

TOPPING UP
REQUIRED

EMPTY

As a guide, a 140 cc reservoir with an adjustable rinse aid setting will disperse between 1 and 5 cc per cycle. This will give around 28 rinses at the highest setting and 140 rinses at the lowest setting. Adjustment will be required to individual machines, corresponding to the varying wash conditions. Too much rinse aid can be as bad as too little. Read the chapter on

Common causes of poor washing results to assist in the correct setting.

The rinse aid dispenser unit

The rinse aid dispenser has two basic styles. One has a combined filler cap and discharge point for the rinse aid dose. More commonly found is the version where the filler and discharge are separate. The latter having a meshed cover to allow the rinse aid liquid through. The tank or reservoir is made of plastic and may vary in shape and style although they all operate in a similar way via an electromagnetic coil similar to the water valve. Some early dishwashers are not fitted with automatic rinse aid dispensers and have to add the rinse aid by hand on the last rinse, (approximately a half teaspoonful).

Where is it found?

Most machines have the reservoir mounted between the inner and outer skins of the door, and only the fill and discharge points are visible on the inner surface of the

door. See: Photo sequence.

Some compact or work-top machines will have the reservoir mounted inside the load compartment as the door is single skin and therefore unable to house the unit.

How does it work?

Within the large refillable reservoir of fixed volume (E), a smaller and adjustable chamber can be seen (B). Adjustment (G) to this chamber varies from type to type (F) i.e. manufacturers may fit more than one make to their range of machines. Sizes and fittings are generally standard although slight variations of dispenser may be found.

Connected to the main body, linking both reservoir and chamber, a solenoid will be found (A). This solenoid is similar to that used on water valves. When energized, the solenoid will discharge the contents of the variable chamber (B) by gravity only. When de-energized, the discharge section of the valve (C) closes and the fill valve (D) opens to refill the variable chamber in readiness for the next programme. (only one operation per wash cycle).

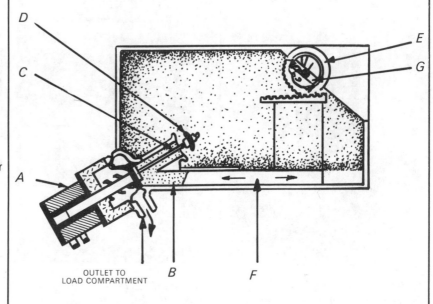

OUTLET TO
LOAD COMPARTMENT

Dishwasher Manual

Problems with rinse aid units

A. A leaking tank, caused by a split can sometimes be sealed, otherwise fit a new unit. Note: The tank/reservoir has to have an air bleed hole on top to allow air in and out when filling and discharging. Do not block or obstruct this small hole in the tank.

B. A fault within the solenoid coil will give similar symptoms to that of a faulty fill valve and dispenses no rinse aid.

C. Valve unit may stick or wear. Such faults may simply require strip down and cleaning. See: Photo sequence.

D. Most faults with the unit will require a full renewal as most manufacturers supply complete units only, no matter what the fault. Strip the unit and clean before opting for renewal. Also test the solenoid as described in *Using a meter*. With a little care, it may be possible to repair the unit instead of replacing it.

Rinse aid repair

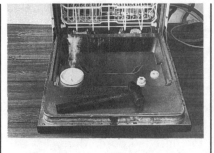

Place a weight on the door inner to hold it in the open position.

With door lowered and counter-weighted remove the outer cover fixing screws.

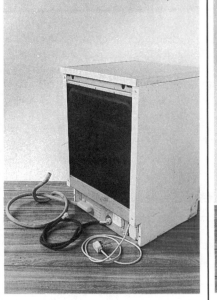

Isolate the machine from the power supply before any repair.

With the door raised, carefully remove the outer door cover to expose the inner section.

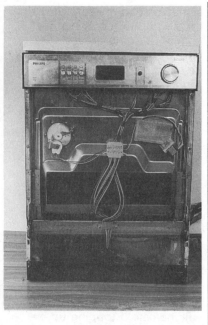

Both rinse aid and powder dispenser are now clearly visible on this Philips machine.

Note and remove the wires to the rinse aid compartment.

Support the rinse aid container and carefully unscrew the plastic securing collars. Take note of any seals.

With the container removed from the door, drain any remaining liquid into a suitable container. (Avoid direct contact with skin and eyes of the concentrated liquid).

In this instance a blockage was suspected as the solenoid coil checked out O.K.

Note the position of the solenoid and screws prior to removal. This is from an Indesit machine.

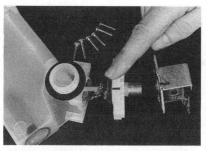

Carefully ease the valve system apart. Lay the parts out in order and clean thoroughly. (Note the large blockage on this valve rubber.)

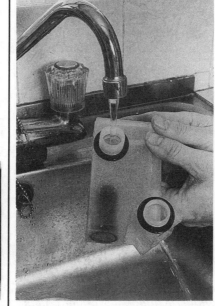

Flush tank thoroughly and clean all the chamber carefully.

Clean valve slide thoroughly to remove solidified rinse aid and particles of dirt, etc. Usage of a good quality rinse aid would reduce these faults from occurring.

Refitting of the rinse aid compartment was a simple reversal of the stripdown procedure. Take care to refit all the seals and not to over tighten the plastic securing collars.

The method of actuating this rinse aid container was by the use of a solenoid valve similar to a water fill valve. An alternative to the solenoid system may be found such as a bimetal strip with a heater coil wrapped around it. When power is supplied to it, the coil heats and the bimetal strip bends. This movement is directly linked to a plunger within the body of the container that dispenses one measured shot of rinse aid liquid per operation.

Faults with this system are identical to the solenoid type. Open circuit element results in no valve operation as would a blockage as shown in the photo sequence.

The wiring and fixing remains identical. Both versions are generally interchangeable.

Note: Care must be taken when removing panels on any dishwasher as the edges of the metal panels are rarely cleanly finished after pressing or moulding. (only areas the user would normally come into contact with gets correctly deburred and finished). Such edges can be extremely sharp, especially on formed stainless steel, so take care not to slip or run fingers along or near the panel edges.

Chapter 27

Pumps – general

Dishwashers in general have two pumps, one large pump called the circulation pump which is used during the wash process to continuously circulate the wash/rinse water and create pressure to drive the spray arms.

The second pump is smaller and less powerful. Its function is to discharge the water from the machine at the end of each wash or rinse.

In some machines however, only one large pump motor may be found which is used for both the circulation and the discharge of water.

a) With the aid of a specially designed impeller, reversal of the main circulation motor will create a lower force discharge, pumping action, therefore eliminating the need for a separate outlet pump.

b) An electromagnetically-operated valve system eliminates the need for two pumps or for the circulation motor to reverse. When emptying is required, the circulation motor runs as normal, but a valve positioned on the outlet hose

Main circulation pump motor. Typical asynchronous induction motor. Styles may vary along with size and water outlet points.

opens and allows a bypass to the normal spray arm feed, and the water will then discharge.

Pumps in greater detail

The main circulation pump is easily recognised by its larger size. It is a single phase asynchronous induction motor. The pump housing is bolted directly on to the motor front end frame with the rotor shaft through its centre. On the back plate of the pump chamber, the rotor shaft passes through a shaft seal which is combined with a carbon or ceramic face seal. A corresponding counter face seal is secured on the impeller which is held on the rotor shaft by a stainless steel bolt (usually left-hand thread), thus giving a rotatable water tight seal.

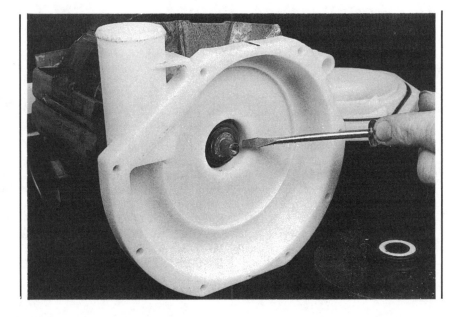

Internal view of a main circulation pump chamber. Shown are the main shaft seal ceramic face of the seal on the impeller.

Induction motor pumps

The most popular type of motor used in today's dishwashing machine is the induction motor which is used because of its quietness and general reliability.

The induction motors in use fall into two categories; 1) Asynchronous induction used for the main motor and 2) Shaded pole induction used for the outlet pump. Most people seem to understand a little about universal motors (motors that require a wound armature and brush gear, etc.), but very little about induction motors of any type.

The asynchronous induction motor is in fact quite simple and uses the absolute basic principles of electricity. Its apparent complexity stems from the need to use extra windings to control its speed. Although modern electronics have allowed for variable control, I deal here with the basics of asynchronous induction motors and those used without module control.

Single phase induction motors consist of two main items – an outer wound coil called a stator (see diagram 1 and 1a)

and a rotatable core made of high grade cast aluminium with internal metal lamination which is slightly askewed to aid torque for starting purposes called the rotor (See diagram 2). The rotor is isolated from the windings and receives no power at all.

The most simple stator would consist of two sets of windings 180 degrees to one another (See diagram 1). Two windings are needed to induce the rotor to turn by their magnetic fields when power is applied. One coil would not induce movement, though if the rotor were started by mechanical means, it would continue to turn as long as power was being supplied to the stator coil. In reality, the motion/starting is induced by placing one set of the windings 90 degrees out of phase with the other. This can be with the use of a relay, but more usually by the use of a capacitor, the rating of which is matched to the windings. The rating is given in microfarads (μF) on its casing. Being out of phase due to the delay caused by the

capacitor/relay, a rotating magnetic field is created causing the rotor to turn up to speed at which point the start windings, as they are known, could be switched out if required. Reversal of the motor is quite simply a reversal of current flow through the start winding or the run winding, but not both.

When a motor, supplied with 240V at 50Hz. (i.e. main voltage), a 2 pole motor mimics the phase cycle and rotates at 50 revolutions per second – i.e. 50 x 60 secs. = 3000 rpm, 4 poles 1500 rpm, 8 poles 750 rpm, 16 poles 375 rpm., variable speeds resulting in complex stator windings and expensive motors. Ensure that faults with motors are checked and rectified promptly. A loose motor block connection may allow power to one winding only and cause over-heating and failure of the whole motor. A faulty capacitor or a malfunction of the programme switches or internal TOC (thermal overload cut-out) of the motor can also have the same result.

Main drawbacks of induction motors

(a) As all of the work is done by a complicated set of windings in the stator, this motor is generally not repairable and must be changed for a new unit.

(b) Capacitor failure often results in the motor failing to run. This often results in burn-out as the rest of the motor windings are receiving power and no rotation is possible. Over-heat is inevitable, even when TOC protected.

Main benefits of induction motors. (Capacitor/relay start)

(a) Generally reliable.
(b) Quiet.
(c) Can be run in both directions.

Warning: When checking for faults, the machine must always by isolated from the mains. Turn off at the wall socket and remove the plug. THE CAPACITOR(S) MAY STILL CONTAIN A CHARGE ALTHOUGH THE MAINS HAS BEEN ISOLATED. THIS MUST BE DISCHARGED BY USING AN ELECTRICALLY INSULATED SCREWDRIVER.

Using this, 'short' the terminals of the capacitor with the shaft of the screwdriver ensuring that you are only in contact with the insulated handle. IT IS NOT SAFE TO PROCEED FURTHER UNTIL THIS HAS BEEN DONE.

If the stator windings of an induction motor are faulty, it may continue to run, although appearing sluggish and getting extremely hot even when used for a short time. Therefore if you have been running the machine to determine the fault, proceed with care as the motor will remain hot for some time. If the motor appears to be very hot, the motor winding may be faulty and the unit should be replaced.

The capacitor – what is it?

The capacitor in a dishwasher is a unit that enables the asynchronous circulation pump to be started.

What does it look like?

Capacitors used in A.C. machines can have either metal or plastic outer casings with an insulated top with two terminals.

How does it work?

What follows is a simplified version of what happens within a capacitor in an A.C. circuit.

The two terminals of the capacitor are in fact completely insulated from one another. Internally they are connected to two sheets of metal foil and between this foil is an insulator. This package of large surface area is rolled into a tube formation which fits into the shell of the capacitor. If the two terminals and their connected sheets of foil are insulated from one another, you may ask – how do they pass a current when in use? The answer is that as the voltage supplied to one terminal is in fact alternating, (i.e. at 50 times per second 50Hz), so therefore is the polarity of its connected foil. An opposite movement of electrons is produced in the other foil even though they are insulated electrically. This effect causes a delay in the electrical path at this point, and this, in the case of an asynchronous induction motor gives the out of phase feed to the start winding.

The storage capacity of a capacitor is measured in microfarads (µF) and is displayed on the shell. Any replacement must be of the same µF rating.

Typical capacitor for use with induction motors. Do not confuse capacitors with suppression units. They may look similar, but their functions differ.

The relay – what is it?

A relay is an electro-mechanical device used in this particular instance for induction motor starting in place of a capacitor.

What does it look like?

The most common relay consists of a plastic moulding with three terminal tags – two at the top and one at its base. On the centre section is a wire wound coil.

How does it work?

The main aim of the relay in the context of asynchronous induction motors is to cause a delay in the start winding supply, similar to the capacitor. The main difference is that the relay achieves this operation mechanically. The wound coil section is connected in series with the run winding. When power is supplied to the motor, the current to the run winding passes through the coil and on to the motor run winding. This current induces a magnetic force in the coil which in turn attracts the metal core of the relay. The metal core is linked to an internal contact switch and when 'made', allows current to pass to the start winding (see diagram). This operation gives the required delay to induce starting of the induction motor.

A relay maybe placed in circuit to cause the phase displacement necessary to start the induction motor. This is a mechanical delay as described and it is essential that the relay is upright when energized.

When power is switched off, gravity resets the relay core. It is, therefore essential that the relay be in its correct position and the machine upright for this item to function correctly.

Faults to watch for are: open circuit of the coil, metal core sticking (in either position), and contact points failing. Renew any suspect relay immediately as the failure of this item can lead to motor failure as with the capacitor.

If you have to renew a damaged stator coil or motor and it is relay started, it is wise to change the relay at the same time as it may (a) have caused the original motor fault or (b) have been subsequently damaged by the motor failure.

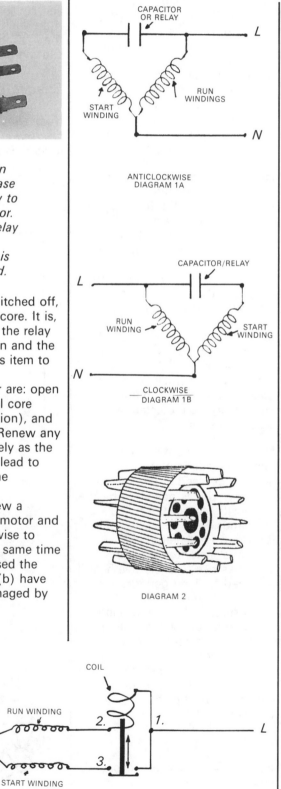

ANTICLOCKWISE
DIAGRAM 1A

CLOCKWISE
DIAGRAM 1B

DIAGRAM 2

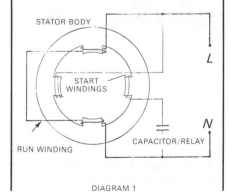

DIAGRAM 1

The shaded pole induction motor

The shaded pole motor is the most simple of all induction motors and is similar in basic format of rotor and stator (See diagram). However, only one stator coil is used to create the magnetic field. Obviously this alone would not induce rotation of the rotor, only a constant magnetic field. To start rotation, an imbalance in the magnetic field is required which is done quite simply by copper band inserts at the pole ends of the stator laminations. The copper band within the mild steel stator laminations distorts the magnetic field in a given direction, therefore inducing rotation in the stator. Reversing the supply to such motors does not effect any change in motor direction as this is governed by the direction of the fixed shaded poles. These motors do not have a high starting torque and because of the magnetic imbalance being fixed, heating of the stator occurs which, under normal conditions creates no problems, but most stator coils are protected by TOC's for safety.

Main drawbacks of induction motors (shaded pole)
(a) Can be used in one direction only. This is governed by the positioning of the pole bands.
(b) Due to the permanent imbalance described, this gives rise to excessive heat if used for long periods.
(c) Low starting power.
(d) If subjected to overheating for long periods, the motor will eventually fail – even if TOC protected.
(e) Generally NOT repairable.
Main benefits of Induction motors (shaded pole)
(a) Very cheap
(b) Very reliable.
(c) Very quiet.

Note TOC = thermal overload cutout.

This means that if the safe working temperature is exceeded, this device will sever the power supply through the motor. Most TOCs are now self re-setting, resulting in constant heating up and cooling down of the motor. If the fault is not spotted quickly, the TOC itself will fail, therefore causing motor failure.

Shaded poles

Note: Connection can be reversed but direction of rotation remains the same. It is governed by the shaded poles only.

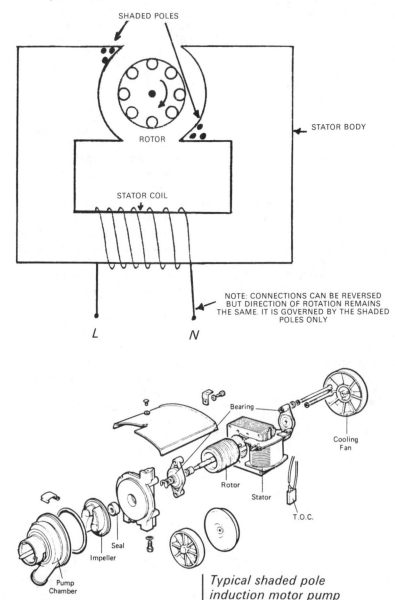

Typical shaded pole induction motor pump

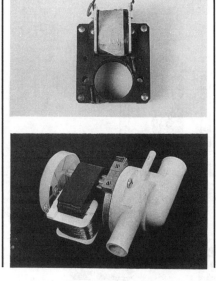

Shown is a shaded pole induction motor stator. The copper banding can be clearly seen.

Typical outlet/drain pump. Large end is the water inlet and the smaller is the outlet. The very small connection on the top is used to flush a small amount of water around the pressure vessel base to help reduce the chance of blockages.

Note: If a shaded pole stator is inadvertently fitted back to front, it will cause the main motor to run in the opposite direction and therefore reduce the pumps efficiency. Always note its orientation prior to stripdown.

Outlet pumps

The pump is a vital part for the correct functioning of the machine and prone to various faults. Leaks from the pumps may not be apparent, but the resulting pool of water usually is. So here are a few points to look out for.

Firstly check all clips on the hoses to and from the pump and tighten if they are loose.

If the leak remains, the pump's shaft seal should be checked. This is the seal that forms a water tight barrier on the rotating shaft of the motor directly between the impeller, and the front motor bearing. The seal can be broken by a scale build-up or food deposits forming on the rotor shaft behind the impeller, thus distorting the rubber seal. To check if this is happening, remove the pump chamber, by removing its securing clips or screws, and whilst securing the rotor of the pump motor, turn the impeller clockwise to undo it from the shaft. (i.e. impeller and rotor are generally left-hand threaded.) Having done this, remove any scale adhering to the shaft and refit, ensuring the pump chamber

seal is in position. If the seal still leaks, this will be due to it being worn or softened. On most machines, this means the complete renewal of the pump (not so costly as you may think, as many genuine and 'pattern' pumps of good quality are now available at very low cost: See *Spares* section). This may seem drastic for such a small seal, but the fact is that water containing detergent would have been entering the front pump bearing long before the leak was bad enough to see. This means it will probably be damaged itself and next in line to cause trouble.

If the rotor shaft was found to be worn, even slightly, e.g. roughness/scoured), it would probably be easier and quicker to fit a complete pump, to avoid any further trouble. In fact this could be the least expensive remedy.

Other leaks can be attributable to the pump, due to impeller damage, that is to say blades of impeller broken off or badly worn away by a solid object lodged in the pump at sometime, (bone or glass fragments are common causes.

Tight bearings may also cause the motor to run slowly).

Any of the above will result in poor water discharge, i.e. slow draining. This in turn may lead to faults such as poor wash results or machine retaining excess water (causing odours). Some machines may leak at certain points on programmes due to filling to too high a level especially those that have a timed fill action at certain stages of the programme.

Checking the impeller and bearings can be done at the same time as checking the seal.

Vortex style pump. Dynamic force exerted on the water in the direction of the outlet.

TO OUTLET HOSE

IMPELLER

PUMP CHAMBER

ROTOR SHAFT

FRONT BEARING

SHAFT SEAL

IMPELLER

VORTEX GAP

FROM SUMP OUTLET

PUMP CHAMBER

VORTEX STYLE PUMP

Above is a simple illustration of the outlet pump chamber and impeller. Water from the sump enters from the front. The rotation of the impeller lifts the water in the direction of the narrower outlet hose. Some machines are fitted with a non-returnable valve system on the outlet hose. Watch out for blockages at that point. There are two types of impeller: one is simply a paddle type and more prone to blockages: the second is like the one illustrated and called a vortex pump. This type of impeller is more of a flat etched disc that allows a gap between itself and the pump chamber. This gap lets particles pass through easier than the bladed impeller version. The vortex impeller applies lift to the water as shown in the smaller version, the action is similar to the rotating vortex created when a bath empties.

Typical outlet pump replacement

Note: Ensure that the machine is isolated before attempting any repair on your dishwasher.

In the following sequence, we show the location of the outlet pump assembly on a Hoover dishwasher and its removal and subsequent renewal. This is then followed by a similar repair to a main circulation pump that illustrates the similarities across the whole range of dishwashers. Only the machines with one pump for both circulation and outlet have any significant differences.

The Hoover machine was leaking badly when inspected, but was in fact still working. When questioned, the user admitted that the machine had been leaking for quite some time,

but now more water seemed to be leaking out than ever before. As you may see, this is obvious in the pictures, by the degree of corrosion to both pump and mounting bracket. (This level of corrosion would have been avoided by earlier detection/report of the initial, much smaller leak.)

Shown in pictures are variations of pumps that may be encountered on this type of machine. The pictures also show the further stripdown of the pump. In this case, it was thought best to renew the pump completely due to the amount of water and detergent damage to both the bearings and metal laminations of the stator. (Again this may have been avoided if the initial leak had been dealt with earlier).

The complete pump was fitted, and the shell and mounts were coated with anti-rust compound prior to the fitting of the pump. Care must be taken that the anti-corrosion liquid does not come into contact with any rubber hoses or seals.

After replacing all hoses and connections (a simple reversal of the removal procedure) the machine was re-positioned into its correct working position and was re-connected to the water and power supply. A short pre-wash programme was selected to ensure that the new pump functioned correctly, to ensure that the re-positioned clips were water tight and that no other leaks were present.

At this point, the user was advised of the unnecessary danger (and damage in this case) caused by using the machine when it obviously had a fault that was ignored.

Note: In most modern machines, the pump has to be changed as a complete unit for even the smallest of problems. This is no excuse for turning a blind eye to such faults. Such behaviour is false economy.

The anti-corrosion coat mentioned can be one of many types available from D.I.Y. care centres and hardware shops. Please use as per manufacturer's instructions, taking care not to allow any contact with rubber hoses or plastics. When using anti-corrosion gel or rubber sealant indoors, care should be taken to protect the floor from spillage, and ensure that adequate ventilation is available.

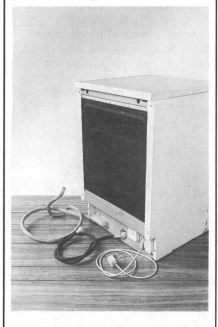

Ensure that machine is isolated and disconnected. Protect the rear and lay the machine carefully on its back.

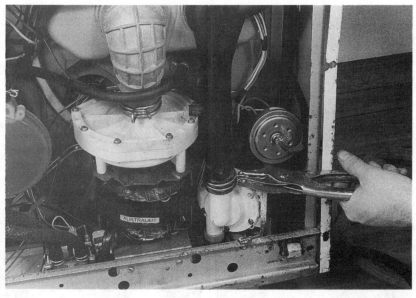

Note and remove the hose clips and connections. Corrosion was found on the mounting. Treat with anti-rust compound prior to refitting.

Machine back protected and carefully laid over. Position of both pumps now clearly seen.

Support pump whilst removing securing bolts and support bracket fixings.

Remove pump carefully from its position.

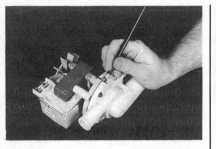

Mark the position of the chamber. Remove the screw holding the pump chamber in position (some machines may have clips).

Water had penetrated the front bearing of this pump.

When fitting a new pump as in this instance, check the bolt sizes. Not all come with bolts as this one did. When reconnecting the terminals, make sure that, if the pump has an earth tag, it is a good fit as with all connections. When the hose and clips have been refitted, the machine is ready for testing on the rinse cycle. Make sure all panels are refitted before commencing functional testing.

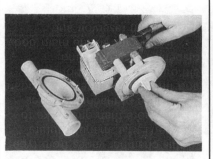

Whilst holding rear shaft securely turn impeller clockwise and remove. (LH hand thread in this instance).

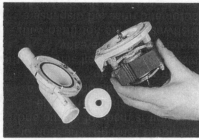

Also the stator laminations are badly corroded.

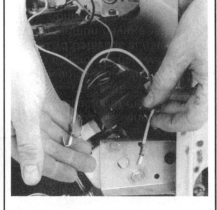

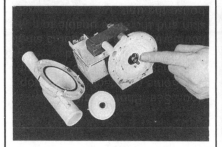

Rear seal exposed. In this case it is badly worn by a build up of scale upon shaft.

A new pump is required for this particular fault.

If a pump has a plastic mounting plate, it is essential that the metal stator laminations are linked to the main machine earth path. Make a short lead to connect the earth tag on the pump to the fixing bolt and secure firmly. Better still, connect to an existing earth point using a piggy back connector.

Main circulation pump fault

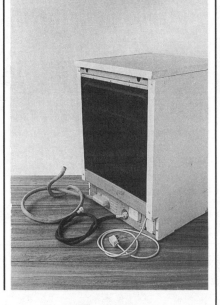

The machine was isolated prior to repair as usual. The reported fault was poor wash and very noisy. As the filters were clean, a faulty circulation pump was suspected, possibly bearings.

The machine was carefully laid on its back to gain access to the large circulation pump motor unit.

Checking the motor and pump required the removal of the whole unit. First the rear fixing screws.

Next the clips securing the hoses were released.

After making a note of all connections and hoses etc., the pump was removed.

Pump chamber was marked to help when time came to refit it. After marking, all the securing screws were removed.

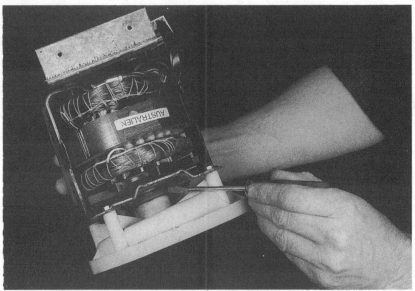

As before, the pump chamber cover was removed to expose the impeller. What was also revealed was the cause of the trouble. A plastic spoon had lodged in the chamber.

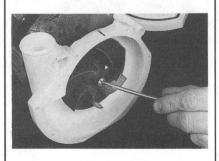

A check was made on the impeller and no damage had been done, but it was thought best to check the face seal at this point so the impeller was removed.

The shaft seal and face seal proved to be OK. Only cleaning was required prior to rebuild.

Refitting was a simple reversal of the stripdown procedure and testing identical to the outlet pump sequence described earlier.

The user of this machine was extremely lucky. If the impeller had jammed solid, the motor would have burnt out and require a complete renewal at a very high cost. This style of motor is of a solid welded construction and cannot be repaired. Even a small

A check on the inner side of the seal confirmed it had not leaked or weeped.

This style of pump can be completely stripped down for repairs, unlike the welded motor shown in the photo sequence. Although the bearings would not be supplied by the machine manufacturer, they can be obtained locally from a bearing stockist by quoting bearing number.

bearing fault caused by a weeping seal would require a complete motor unit. Most manufacturers seem to adopt the complete unit change philosophy and only supply shaft seals and impellers as service items. If the motor bearings fail and the motor is of the none welded type which can be stripped down, a trip to the local bearing stockist with the old bearing should result in new ones being obtained with very little trouble as they are generally a common size.

Chapter 28

Timers (programmers)

The programmer (or timer, as it is more commonly known,) is the unit located at the top of the machine, directly behind the selector knob. This can be situated on the door or on a panel above the door as with some Indesit models. (With machines that have door mounted timers, it is essential that the wiring harness section is read prior to suspecting a timer fault).

When a programme is selected, the timer follows a pre-determined sequence switching components in and out (i.e. heater, pump, valves), for various lengths of time. Due to the apparent complexity of this component, it wrongly tends to be regarded as a "no go" area.

The intention of this manual has been to show that the dishwashing machine is not so mysterious, and when broken down into its constituent parts, its simplicity of operation is revealed. To describe the workings of the timer in your dishwasher we would need to know the make, model number, date of manufacture and the timer number itself. These are needed to ascertain which variation of timer and associated variation of programmes that your particular machine has. In their most infinite wisdom, the manufacturers have seen fit to change their timers, numbers and wiring colours etc., with regularity.

The timer/programmers used in dishwashers are similar to those used in automatic washing machines. They are generally more compact and contain fewer switch banks due to the less complicated wash actions carried out by the dishwasher. They have fewer specialised programmes than their clothes washing counterparts. Though smaller and less complex their replacement cost is often higher than the automatic washing machine.

To give detailed information about the unit that is in your particular machine, a book several times the size of this one would be needed. What follows is a general description of how timers work, some of the most common faults and their symptoms.

How a Crouzet timer works

What follows is a description of how a Crouzet timer works. This is one of the most common timers and is found in more than fifty percent of the machines sold in Britain today. The Crouzet is an edge cam timer, which means that each switch within the timer is operated by its own cam on a central rotatable barrel. This allows switches to be dropped or lifted into different positions at the same time. This operation can be likened to that of the old style pianola or musical box that played a tune with the aid of a cylinder. If the cylinder were to be changed, a different tune would be produced. The same principle applies to the timer. Although the external appearance of the timer does not change, a simple change of the central barrel will give the manufacturer a different switching sequence and therefore a different machine to put on the market. Because of this, when changing the timer it is important that the correct version is used. i.e, one with the same central barrel. This is shown by the serial number on the timer.

On the central barrel there are several cams, with each cam having two corresponding switches. The barrel is rotated by the cam advance motor, which is energised by impulse commands such as that from the thermostat. i.e, if the selected temperature is reached, the thermostat closes, thus causing the motor to run.

The motor will continue to run until a cam position is reached that breaks the impulse path (motor circuit). The barrel is then in the correct position for the next sequence of instructions.

The Crouzet is normally a 45 step cycle. This means that on one complete revolution of the cam, it will have initiated 45 switches (45 'clicks'). A variation to this, is one of 60 step cycles.

Next to the advance motor is the timing motor, which times all of the functions of the machine. i.e. Washing, emptying, etc. The timing motor drives a timing cam which, via internal gearing, turns one revolution every minute. Therefore a six minute wash consists of six, one minute timing requests.

An emptying cycle would consist of supplying power to the outlet pump for one minute and moving to the next cam position. Most dishwasher timers use a one minute time cycle, unlike their counterparts in automatic washing machines which use two minute time cycles, (due to the larger quantity of water used and variations of wash times required).

Cams operate the switches in the timer. For example, at the correct point in the programme, the cam on which the heater switch rests will allow the switch to make, therefore engaging the heater. The cam will also engage the correct thermostat switch for that programme. When the correct heat is reached and the timer has timed out, the thermostat then impulses the cam advance motor. In English, this is read as "When the temperature is reached, finish timing and then impulse (move) onto the next cam position."

An alternative to the two motor Crouzet, is the one motor version, where the one motor does both of the jobs via the cams. This version is common in the Indesit, Zanussi, Candy, etc.

With a little imagination, it should be quite clear how a programme actually works, not by some mysterious phenomena, but by a sequence of simple movements that combine to form a complete operational programme.

How a face cam timer works

The same basic principles apply, only the switches are operated by an etched disc that allows the switches to drop in and out of the recessed positions on its face. Face cam timers are of the one motor variety as described above.

The timers are easily identifiable by the fact that an edge cam timer is much longer and deeper than the face cam. This is because the face cam timer is much slimmer due to the fact that only one disc is used to operate all of the switches. The slim lines of face cam timers make them more popular on door mounted machines.

The main drawbacks of timers:
(a) Units cannot be repaired. Complete unit changes are needed for timer faults.
(b) Without detailed information of the switching sequences of the faulty timer, faults are difficult to trace as a combination of switches may be used.
(c) Units can often be difficult to fit. (Unless a logical approach is used!)

The main benefits of timers:
(a) Modern timers are very reliable.
(b) New units are relatively low in cost.
(c) Dishwasher timers are easier to fit than those of the automatic washing machine as they have fewer switch banks and connecting wires, i.e. much smaller harness.

It must be remembered that when a fault is suspected, it is not always the most complicated component that can cause the most trouble. If a process of elimination is used and all other parts of the machine are found to be working correctly, it is only then that the timer should be suspected. (Unless of course in the case of obvious failure, such as a burn out or damage to the timer.)

Note: Ensure that the power is turned off and that the plug is removed from its socket at all times. Do not remove the timer from the machine at this point.

The removal and subsequent exchange of the timer can be a long and tedious task. Allow enough time to complete the job – do not rush.

Do not remove any wiring as yet, but thoroughly check for any overheating of the connections to and from the timer spades (Connections). i.e. If a fault is suspected in the heater switch, trace the wire from the heater to the timer. This gives the location of the heater switch, and should be examined for any signs of burning or being loose. (This would at least confirm your suspicions.)

Having decided that the timer is at fault, a note should be taken of all of the numbers that are on the timer, together with the make, model and age of your machine.

Armed with this information, you can obtain an exact replacement. See *Buying spare parts* chapter.

When the replacement has been obtained, visually check that they are identical, as timers will not be exchanged by any known company, once they have been fitted. (You have been warned!) Having confirmed that it is the correct replacement, and that any accompanying instructions have been read thoroughly, you can proceed to swap the wiring. The only way that this can be done is by placing the new timer in the same place as the original, swapping the wires on a one-to-one basis. (Although very time consuming, this is by far the safest method.) A mistake at this point would be almost impossible to rectify without a wiring and timer diagram, therefore it is

Types of timer internal switches.

Cam Follower Down = A-C
Connections Made

Edge Cam
Switch

Cam Follower Up = A-B
Connections Made

Etched Disc

Cam Follower

Switch as A-B
As A-C

Face cam timer.

advisable to ask a colleague to supervise operations. When all connections have been successfully exchanged, the timer can be fitted into position, ensuring that any parts that are connected to salt indicators, etc., are positioned correctly. Once fitted into position, and the covers have been refitted, the power can be turned on, and a test programme can be implemented.

Note: Some timers have small metal clips that join/link terminals together. These do not come with the new timer. Ensure they are swapped from the original. To avoid the possibility of error, detailed notes or drawings should be made prior to removing any connections or wiring. Unmarked wires should be tagged with their switch bank number.

Timer variations

The timers shown are a small selection that are used in today's automatic dishwashing machines.

A manufacturer may have numerous variations of the same timer. For instance, although your timer may be a Crouzet, your neighbour may have the same machine with seemingly the same timer in it, but in fact, it may be a variations of the same timer. These variations are identifiable by the slight difference in serial numbers shown on the timer. This illustrates the need to obtain the exact number of your timer and machine when a replacement is to be obtained.

Some machines have push buttons only to select the required programme and no visible selector knob. The switch/button bank usually consists of an "ON/OFF" button, a series of selector buttons for various wash types and combinations, and a start button. On this sort of machine, the timer is of a similar type to those described earlier and can be of the face or edge cam variety.

The buttons act as bypasses to sections of the programme, for instance, the selection of a pre-wash cycle will allow the timer to advance to that position missing out all the steps before and after it when the start button is pressed. Sometimes a combination of switches can be

used but all act as "impulse" or "bypass" depending on the length and type of wash required by the user. In reality, the buttons select the required programme in place of the user manually turning the timer shaft via the selector knob.

The functional parts of the machine differ little from machines with conventional selector knobs. This also applies to machines with micro processor control units which are recognisable by the digital displays used to show programme in use and programme selection. These machines sometimes display an error code when faults occur which relate to a table in the handbook. Micro processor timers are more complex to fault locate and cannot be easily checked. It is best to eliminate all other possible causes of faults before suspecting the actual unit. If all the other checks prove satisfactory, then check all connections to and from the control boards, (the micro processor generally has two – one low voltage board for the processor itself, and one power board with relays to operate the mains voltage switching which the processor cannot do directly).

The connections to printed circuit boards are prone to oxidization giving poor electrical contact on the low voltages used by the programme boards.

If the fault remains after the above checking, the only option left is to change the unit as it is most likely to be a failure in the circuitry. Do not touch the processor board's components at all as they are sensitive to static electricity and are easily damaged by careless handling. The power boards are more robust but care must still be exercised when handling them.

The power board is generally much bigger and houses a large transformer to drop the voltage to the processor. Electronic circuit faults occur more often with power boards as the power to operate the pump, heater, etc., is switched mechanically by relays operated by the lower voltage supplied from the programme board, i.e., processors themselves cannot directly switch mains power and use mechanical relays. Try to isolate if a mechanical fault is suspected, (simply the heater not receiving power, etc.)

Note: All checks must be carried out with the machine isolated in the usual manner – taps off, plug out! Under no circumstances should you try to test the processor board, even with a low voltage tester because the microprocessor chip can easily be damaged.

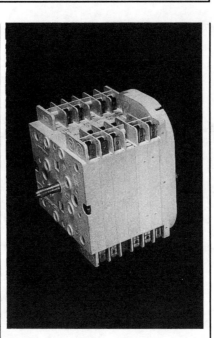

Two distinct types of Crouzet timers can be found. The segmented type – left and the edge block type – right.

Crouzet timers have either a large code number on the top of the timer or a smaller, longer number on the left-hand side. When ordering a new item all numbers that are on the timer should be quoted together with the make, model and serial number of your machine.

Internal view of switch bank. Note switch movements and cam position (Crouzet timer)

Edge block switch bank showing clearly the switch arrangement and cam followers. Switch operation is the same, only the style of mounting is different.

Indesit Crouzet timer with one switch block removed showing cam barrel.

Internal view of cam barrel. Each row is for one switch block and has three levels.

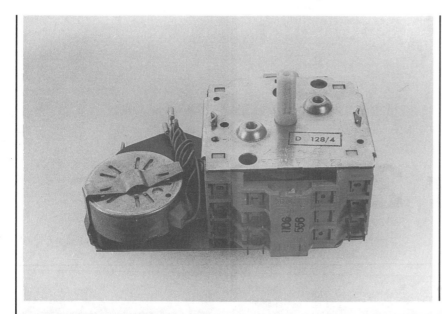

This is a Zanussi Z30 series timer. It has a very simple 'one' block connector that is easily fitted. Take care that connections within the harness block do not slide out when it is pushed on timer. The timer motor is located beneath the unit and drives the cam via an elongated gear system. This saves on overall depth of the unit.

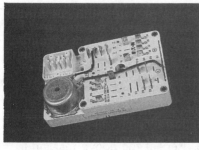

Typical face cam timer (terminals on rear).

The drive motor of this timer is internally fitted in to the cam barrel to keep size to a minimum. It is also fitted with edge block connector for the single switch bank.

Candy timer again shown with cover removed to highlight similar cam operation, this time with two banks and simple tag connections.

One motor Crouzet type timer in situ on this Candy machine. Size of timer is not important on this model as the timer is fitted beneath the top of the machine, not in the door.

Chapter 29

Low insulation

What is low insulation

Low insulation is best described as a slight leak to earth of electricity from the wiring of one or more of the components or wiring in an earthed appliance. If very slight, this will not harm the appliance but is an indication of faults to come and should be corrected immediately for safety reasons. The condition occurs during the progressive breakdown of the insulating properties of a normally electrically leakproof system.

How is it caused?

This can be caused by normal wear and tear over a long period, resulting in a breakdown of the insulating coating on wiring, motor windings, heater elements, etc. Such a breakdown of insulation may not result in a failure of this part at this stage and the appliance may still function as normal. This, however, is not an excuse to ignore low insulation; failure to trace and rectify low insulation is foolhardy because it compromises safety. Also extra expense is likely to be incurred in the long run. Faulty covers or misplaced seals can allow dust or damp to penetrate motor windings resulting in low insulation. If not corrected, this could lead to a complete failure of the motor, or worse. A simple renewal of the cover or seal and careful cleaning and drying of the Thermal Overload Cut-out (TOC) and windings may be all that is needed to save money and improve safety for all concerned.

How can it be detected?

When an engineer tests for low insulation, he will use an instrument called a low insulation tester. The law requires repair engineers to test for low insulation, and there is a minimum allowable level as follows:

1. Between the earth pin on the plug and all earth connection points within the appliance, the maximum resistance should be 1 ohm, i.e. no resistance – a perfect connection.
2. With the machine unplugged, select a wash programme and turn the machine on. Leave one lead of the test meter connected to the earth pin of the plug and use the other lead to bond (join) the live and neutral pins on the plug. The minimum resistance should be 2 megohm, i.e. very high resistance – no connection at all.
3. Repeat the above test, after setting the machine to a rinse programme. (Remember the machine's heater is normally only supplied with power when the correct level of water has been reached, it is wise, therefore, to test the heater separately).
4. Testing of the heater can be carried out by removing both wiring connections to the heater. Connect one lead of the test meter to one of the free terminals and the other lead to the earth terminal, again the minimum resistance should be 2 megohm. Repeat the test using the other terminal.

These tests are carried out using a meter designed to test insulation by applying a high voltage (500 v) at a very low ampèrage (for safety). It is an unfortunate fact that many engineers do not possess such a device, and therefore do not check for low insulation. This does not mean that you should

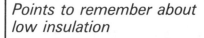

not! A meter to test for low insulation would cost upwards of £150 and therefore out of reach of most DIY repairers. An alternative is to utilise an in-line circuit breaker (*see* Flowchart). The appliance is plugged into the circuit breaker, which is then plugged into the socket. If an RCD already protects the circuit or socket then it can be used as the tester. As mentioned in *'Basics – electrical'*, the purpose of the device is to detect low insulation or leakage to earth and turn off the power to the appliance. Although this is not the ideal way of testing for low insulation, it will help in locating it and provide safety for the appliance and its user.

If any appliance trips an RCD (or similar) system, do not use the appliance until the fault has been rectified. If tripping occurs with no appliances or load on the system, then a fault on the house wiring is indicated and the trip switch should not be reset until the fault is found and corrected.

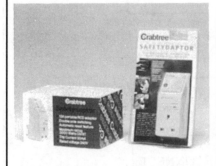

A quality double pole portable (adaptor type) RCD.

Points to remember about low insulation

Ensure that any disconnection or removal of wires is safe, and not earthing via another wire or the shell of the machine, etc.

When disconnecting any wires during the testing of low insulation, it should be remembered that the machine must be isolated from the mains at all times, and the panels must be replaced before the machine is re-tested.

Before testing for low insulation with the use of a circuit breaker, all earth paths of the machine should be tested. This is done by connecting a meter between the earth pin of the plug, and all other metal parts of the machine in turn. Maximum resistance should be 1 ohm. See *Electrical circuit testing* (Using a meter).

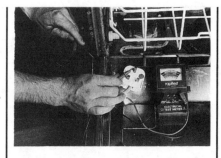

Getting ready to check for earth continuity from earth pin on the plug to the door hinge. As circuit is as yet incomplete, meter reads 'NO' circuit.

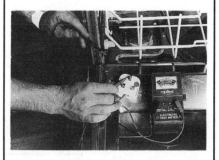

When the probe is connected to metal of the door hinge, the needle swings across to indicate a complete or closed circuit. This confirms that the earth path is complete from the plug terminal to the metal hinge as it should be. If this test fails, investigate and cure the open circuit and do not use the machine until the fault is rectified. It is always advisable to check that all the items that have earth connections pass this earth continuity check, i.e., have a perfect earth path. Do not forget to check the plug also has a good earth. (See Plug in tester).

LOW INSULATION FLOWCHART

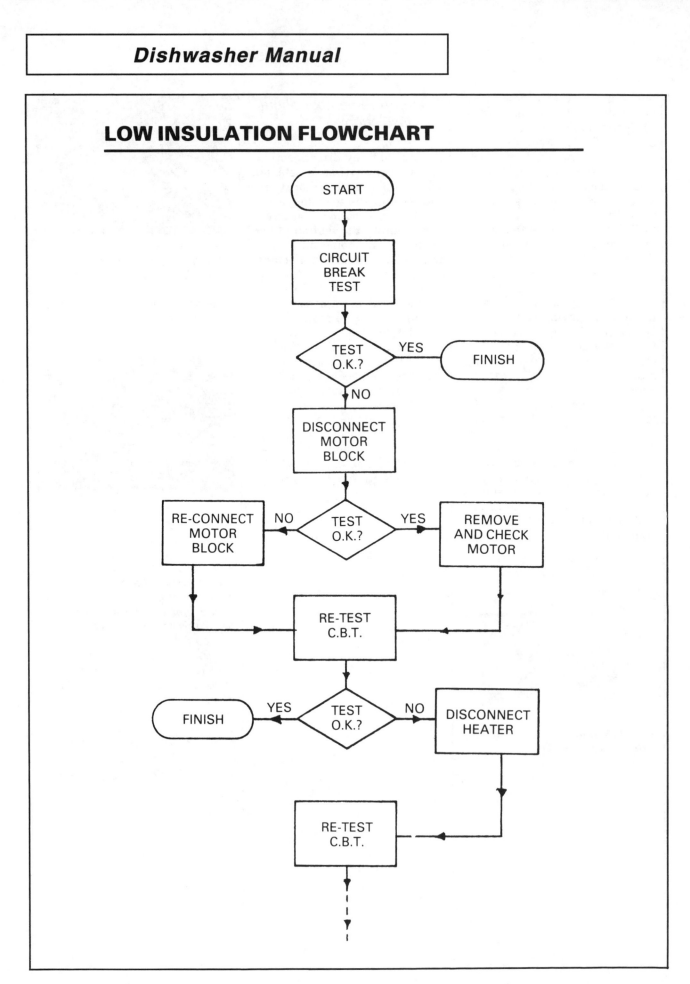

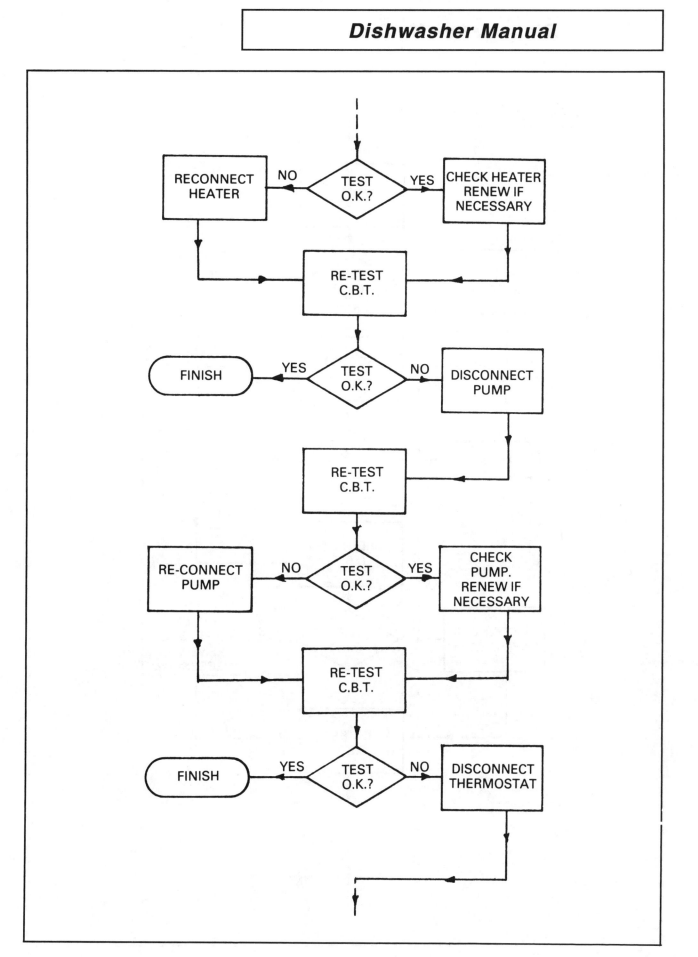

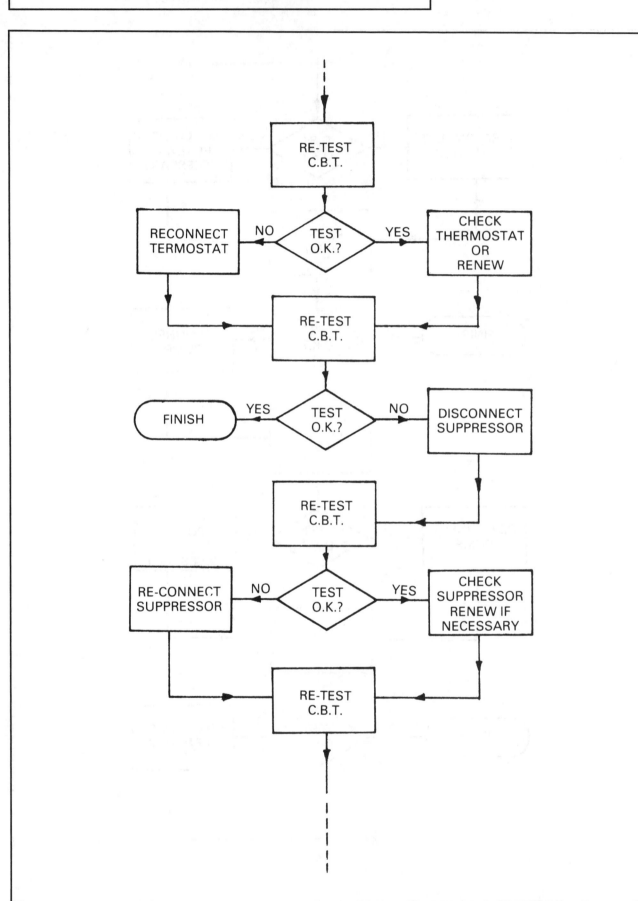

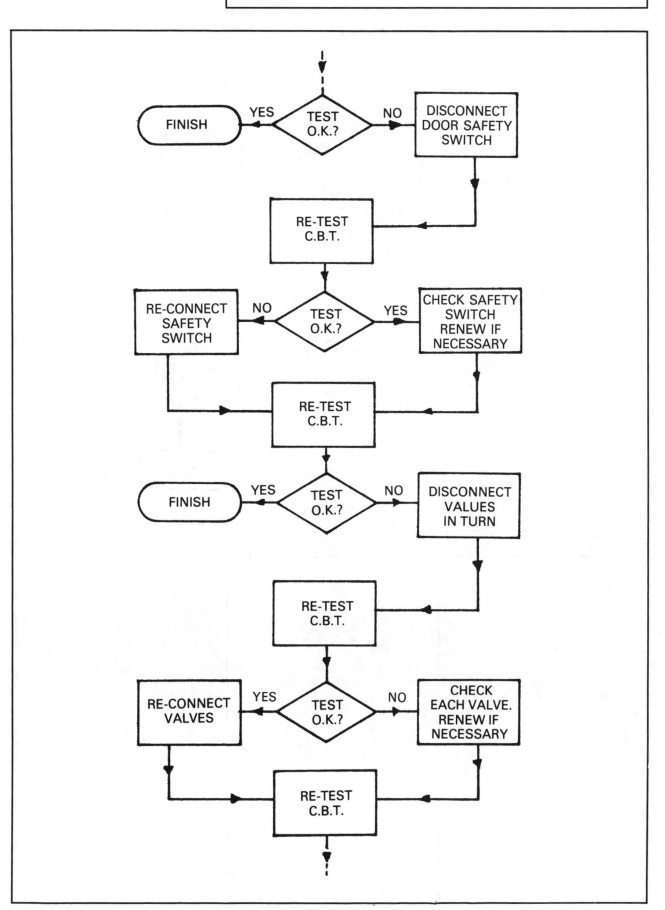

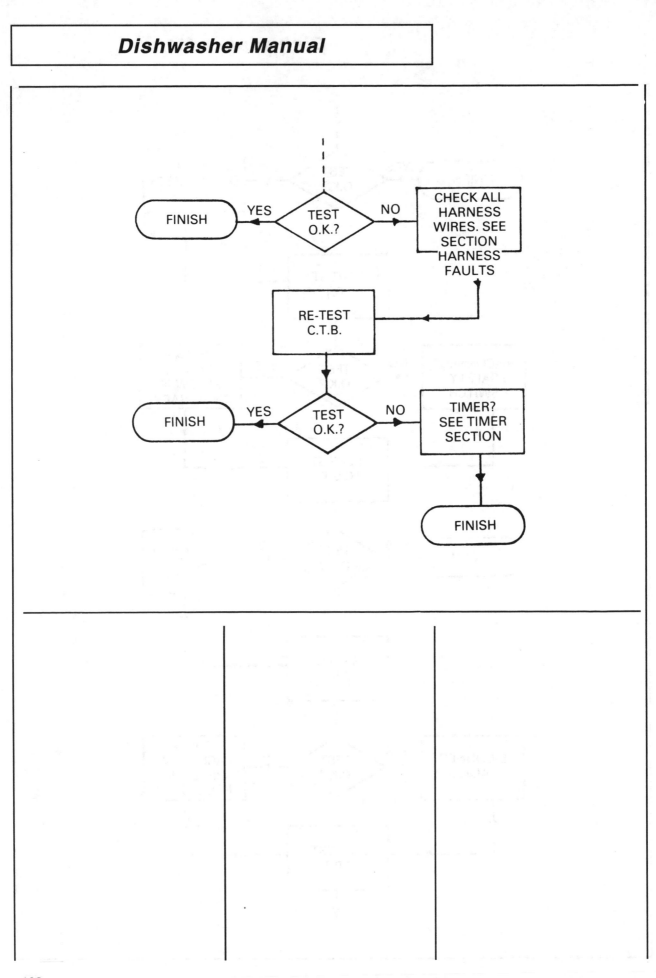

Chapter 30

The suppressor

What is a suppressor?

A suppressor is a device designed to eliminate the formation and transmission of spurious radio waves that may be produced by the operation of switches and motors within the appliance during its normal operation. When switching occurs within the machine and it is not suppressed, small sparks at the contact points may produce interference on radio and T.V. channels.

Why should all machines have them?

By law, all domestic appliances must be suppressed to conform to the regulations on radio interference, and it is an offence to use a machine not suppressed to these standards.

Where is it located?

Suppressors vary in style, shape, size and colour. Sometimes individual parts are suppressed, but more often the mains supply is suppressed at or just after the entry point into the machine. This is called 'in-line' suppression as both the live and neutral supply goes through the suppressor and on to supply the whole of the machine with power.

Do not confuse the suppressor with the capacitor that may be in the machine. They may look very similar but carry out distinctly different functions.

The suppressor can also be called a mains filter because of its filtering effect of removing spurious radio transmission.

Faults with suppressors (filters)

The main fault is one of short circuiting to earth usually resulting in the unit "blowing" both the main fuse and itself. This is often accompanied by a pungent burnt smell. Renewal is a straight forward one-for-one replacement.

Open circuit problems can occur and the unit will fail to allow current to pass through as normal. The suppressor can easily be checked for continuity using a meter. See *Using a meter* section in Chapter 31. When checking, inspect the top insulation closely and if cracked or at all suspect, renew complete unit.

In-line suppressors use the earth path as part of their filtering circuit, (although very little power passes through it). It is essential for ALL machines to have a good earth path. If a machine with an in-line suppressor/filter has a break in its earth path (due to cable, plug or socket fault) small electric shocks may be experienced when the user touches metal parts of the machine, especially if they are in touch with a good earth themselves (i.e. holding metal sink or work top when bending down to machine etc.). It is essential that such faults are traced and corrected immediately. Always ensure that any electrical appliance has a correctly wired plug and that all sockets have a good earth path. See: *Basics – electrical*.

A revised version of suppressor may be found in addition to those described above. This is an induction coil, fitted in series between the neutral position at the terminal block and the shell of the machine. As an induction coil is of far heavier gauge, it only passes suppression current whereas the two earlier versions carry the full voltage load. Because of this the temperature rises and associated problems are reduced in the new induction type. On some machines, a combination of both old and new types of suppressor may be found.

Suppressors should not be bypassed or omitted, as to have an unsuppressed machine is an offence because of the interference that it may cause to others.

In line suppressor unit

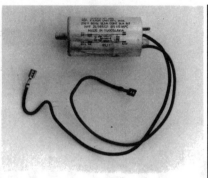

Variation of style of suppression unit. One of many such variants.

Chapter 31

Electrical circuit testing

Using a meter

Throughout this book, references are made to meters and their use in continuity testing of individual parts of the appliance and their connecting wires. All such testing and checking for 'open' (not allowing for current flow), or 'closed' circuit (allowing current to flow), must be carried out using a battery-powered multi-meter or test meter. Testing should **NEVER** be carried out on live items, ie appliances connected to the mains supply. Remember, completely isolate the appliance from the mains supply before starting any repair work or testing.

Although some meters or testers have the facility to check mains voltages, I do not agree with their use in repairs to domestic appliances. Faults can be easily traced by simple low-voltage (battery power) continuity testing, proving that the simplest of meters or even a home-made one like the one described below are perfectly adequate. Remember that safety is paramount and in no circumstances should it be compromised. Always double-check that the appliance is unplugged – a good tip is to

keep the plug in view so that no-one else can plug it in unbeknown to you.

If you decide to buy a test meter do not be tempted to get an over-complicated one as it could end up confusing and misleading you when in use. Before using your new meter, read the manufacturer's instructions thoroughly and make sure that you fully understand them. The meter used in the photographs is simple to use when continuity testing and has a scale that reads 'open' circuit or 'closed' circuit. It was purchased from a local DIY store and was very reasonably priced. The meter will also help locate faults with car electrics, but as previously stated, using on live mains circuits should not be entertained.

Some multi-meters are able to show the resistance value of the item being tested as well as indicating continuity. This can be extremely useful if the correct value of the item being tested is known although this is by no means essential. Detailed use of the multi-meter for this function will be found in its accompanying instruction leaflet.

A simple continuity tester

This simple device can be used to trace wiring faults in most appliances and is very easy to make. It uses the lack of continuity to its full advantage. To make this tester, you will need a dry torch battery, a bulb of the same voltage and three wires (1 x 5 inch and 2 x 10 inch). Connect the short wire to the positive terminal of the battery and the other end of that wire to the centre terminal of the torch bulb. Attach one of the longer wires to the negative terminal of the battery and leave the other end free. The other wire should be attached to the body of the bulb and again, leave the end free.

The two loose ends now act as the test wires on the tester. Press the two ends of the wire together, and the bulb will light. When testing an open circuit the light will stay OFF, and when testing a 'closed circuit' the light will be ON.

Ensure that the machine is isolated from the main supply before attempting to use a meter.

Note: Low voltage bulb type testers of 1½ volts or 3 volts are unable to test the continuity of many components and should be used mainly for wiring fault finding. A test meter like the one shown is required to test components for continuity, i.e. motors, heaters, etc.

How to test for continuity

To test for an open circuit in a component, note and remove the original wiring to the component to be tested. (If this is not done, false readings may be given from other items that may be in circuit.) The ends of the two probes (of the meter) should be attached to the suspect component. For example, to test a heater for continuity, place the probes on the tags at the end of the heater and watch the meter. This needle should move. At this stage, it does not matter if the needle does not reach zero.

If the heater is open circuit (no movement) the heater can then be suspected and tested further. If closed circuit, the heater is OK.

Often the most effective way to trace a fault is to use a very simple but logical approach to the process. One such approach is called the leap frog method and can be used to find the failed/open circuit part or parts. In this instance, let us assume that the appliance does not work at all when tested, therefore we cannot deduce where the problem lies purely

from the symptoms. A quick check of the supply socket by plugging in another appliance known to be OK will verify (or not) that there is power up to that point. This confirms that the fault lies somewhere in the appliance, its flex or plug. We know that during normal conditions, power flows in through the live pin on the plug, through the appliance (when switched on) and returns via the neutral pin on the plug.

The fact that the appliance will not work at all even when plugged in and switched on indicates that an open circuit exists somewhere along this normal live-to-neutral circuit. Leap frog testing, using a continuity meter, would be as follows. First, test that the meter

is working correctly, i.e. touch test probes together and the meter should indicate continuity. Connect one probe to the live pin of the isolated appliance's plug and the other on the live conductor connecting point in the plug. Continuity will be found when the pin, fuse and their connections are all OK. If this check proves OK, move the probe from the live conductor point in the plug to the live conductor connection in the terminal block within the appliance. Again, continuity should be found, if not, a fault between plug and terminal block is indicated. When continuity testing flex, the wire should be moved continuously, bending it back and forth along the length, so that wire breakage internally –

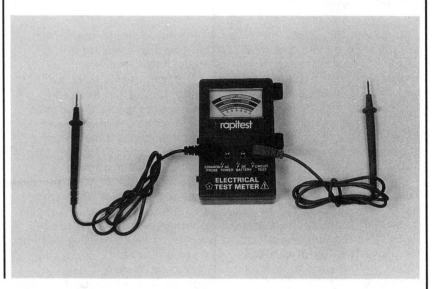

A typical multimeter of the type to be bought in most DIY stores. Try to obtain a meter with a good information booklet. The meter shown was purchased for under £14.00 and proved to be useful for many other jobs around the house and car.

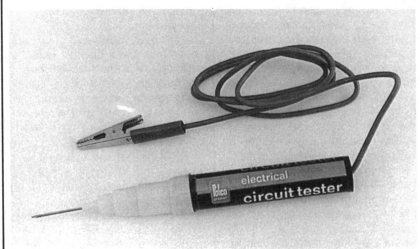

This simple continuity tester was purchased from a local automart for only £2. It is a manufactured version of the home-made type described.

which often causes intermittent continuity – can be checked. If this test is OK, move the probe to the next convenient point along the live conductor, in this instance, the supply side of the door safety switch. Again, continuity is required. An open circuit indicates a fault between terminal block and switch connection. The next step is to move the probe to the opposite terminal of the switch. Operate the switch to verify correct action (i.e. ON continuity, OFF open circuit). At this point we will assume that an open circuit has been indicated in the ON position, so go back to the last test point and verify continuity up to that point. If found to be OK, then a fault has been traced that lies within the switch.

This simple, methodical approach is all that is required to find such problems. With more complex circuits it is best to break them down into individual sections, i.e. motor, heater, switch, etc., and test continuity of each section from Live through the individual parts and back to Neutral. This may involve moving the live probe that would normally remain on the plug live pin to a more convenient supply point within the appliance to avoid misleading continuity readings by other items within the appliance circuit. With practice, faults can be found even in complex wiring in this way.

For your convenience, the correct states of several components are listed below.

Component	Typical resistance	Special notes
Plug fuse	None	Check correct rating and condition of plug, fuse and socket, Change if found to be defective in any way.
Inlet valves	3500 – 5000 ohms	If the circuit is OK, possible manual fault inside valve.
Heater	22 ohms	Check also for low insulation
Pressure switch	Only open or closed circuit	See water level control *Pressure switch* section
Thermostat	-	See *Thermostat* section
Outlet pump	45 ohms	If the circuit is OK., possible manual fault inside pump.
Main motor	Start winding Run winding	Refer to Pumps section for help.
Harness wiring	None	Test each wire separately to suspect component, pulling connections and along its length to find possible internal open circuit. Outer insulation may however appear complete.
Rinse aid solenoid	3500 – 5000 ohms	Check also for manual fault and blockages.
Detergent solenoid	3500 – 5000 ohms	Check also for manual fault and blockages.

A simple continuity test (i.e. for 'closed' circuit) on this timer motor coil confirmed that it was in fact 'open' circuit and that the timer failed to advance through the programme. The test could have been easily made with the timer *in situ*, but is shown here removed from the machine for clarity. Note: Most manufacturers would supply a complete timer unit for such a fault though it is sometimes possible to obtain the motor coils from pattern spares stockists. Fitting of such a coil is possible. With a little care, ease the metal outer cover off, refit securely by pressing together firmly.

The test on this pump stator proved to be OK, (i.e. closed circuit continuity). This meant that the supply or neutral to and from the pump required checking to discover the reason why the pump failed to work at any point in the programme.

The ohms reading will differ from item to item. Test for open or closed circuits only. Any reference to an ohm (Ω) reading is a guide only as resistances differ from machine to machine. The objective is to test for either continuity or the lack of continuity of the item being tested.

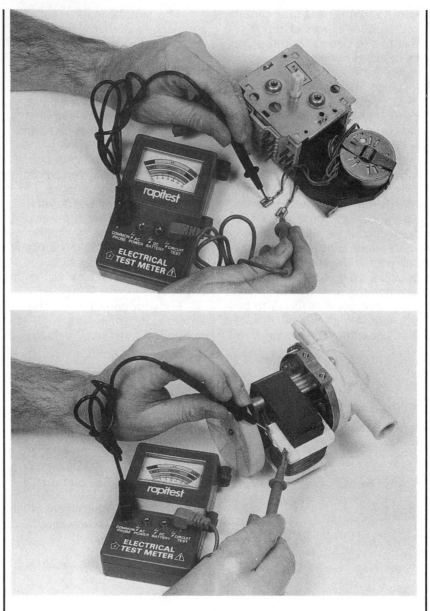

Chapter 32

Wiring harness faults

What is a wiring harness?

The term harness is used for all of the wires that connect the various components within the machine. They are usually bound or fastened together in bunches to keep the wiring in the machine neat and safely anchored.

What does it do?

At first sight, the harness may look like a jumble of wires thrown together. This is not the case. If you take the time to inspect the harness, you will find that each wire is colour coded or numbered (either on the wire itself, or on the connector at either end). This allows you to follow the wire through the machine easily. With practice, any wiring codings can be followed.

As most of the wires in the machine either finish or start at the timer unit, it may be helpful to think of the timer as the base of a tree, with the main wiring harness as the trunk. As the trunk is followed, branches appear (i.e. wires to the valve, pressure switches, etc.). As the trunk continues upwards, it slowly gets thinner and branching takes place to the motor, pump, etc.

Each item is therefore separate, but linked to the timer by a central bond of wire. This can be likened to a central command post, communicating with field outposts.

The connecting wires to and/or from a component are vital to that component and possibly others that rely on that items correct functioning. Luckily, wiring faults are not too common. When these faults do occur, they usually seem to result in big problems, when in truth only a small fault has occurred, i.e., one poor connection can cause a motor not to function at all, and render the machine unusable. Do not fall into the trap of always suspecting the worst. Many people, including engineers, blindly fit parts such as a motor or a valve for a similar fault to that mentioned, only to find it did not cure the problem. Unfortunately the timer is usually blamed and subsequently changed. This does not cure the problem and is an expensive mistake. Stop, think and check all wires and connections that relate to your particular fault. Always inspect all connections and ensure that the wire and connector are tightly joined. Loose or poor connections can

overheat and cause a lot of trouble, especially on items such as the heater.

Poor connections to items such as the rinse aid, detergent dispenser and door micro switch will be aggravated by the movement of the door when used and may not be so apparent when the test is carried out.

One of the most difficult faults to find is where the metal core of the wire has broken and the outer insulation has not. This wire will appear perfect from the outside but will pass no electrical current. To test for this, see Chapter 31. This fault on dishwashers usually occurs at the base of the door where the wiring enters to supply items mounted within the door, such as rinse aid and detergent dispensers, etc. If the timer unit is situated in the door, all the wires must therefore at some point pass a fixed point to a movable one on the door. Although the manufacturers normally fit some form of protection at this point, it has to allow for the flexing of the cable during normal opening and closing of the door. It is this flexing that inevitably leads to a break in either the inner core or outer insulation of one or more of the wires present. Check and inspect thoroughly all points at which wiring enters or leaves the door base. Renew any suspect faulty covers or supports, etc. If a break or crack in the insulation is found at this point, renew the whole of the wire in question whenever possible. DO NOT simply tape or join the damaged wire at that point. As with any repair, ensure that the machine is completely isolated before this or any repair or inspection is carried out.

It must be remembered that such faults may be intermittent. That is to say that one reading may be correct and the same test later may prove incorrect. This is due to the movement of the outer insulation of the wire first making, then breaking the electrical connection.

When testing for such intermittent faults, it is wise to pull or stretch each wire tested, as an unbroken wire *will not* stretch. A wire that is broken *will* stretch at the break point and rectification is a simple matter of renewing the connection with a suitable connector. Take time to do a few simple checks – it saves time, patience and money.

Note: Ensure that the harness is secured adequately to the shell of the machine, but allow a little slack to such items as the motor, heater, etc. Take care that any metal fastening clips do not chafe the plastic insulation around the wires. Also make sure that the wires are not in contact with sharp metal edges such as self-tapping screws.

WARNING: Before attempting to remove or repair the wiring harness or any other component in the machine, isolate the machine from the main electrical supply by removing the plug from the wall socket.

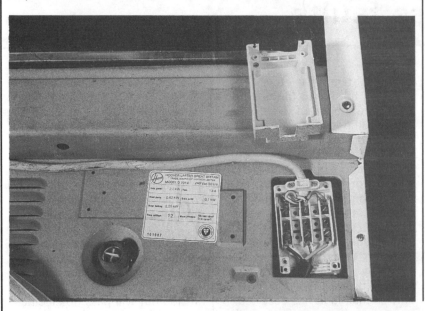

The terminal block is the first distribution point of the power into the machine. Ensure all connections are sound as heat will be generated if not.

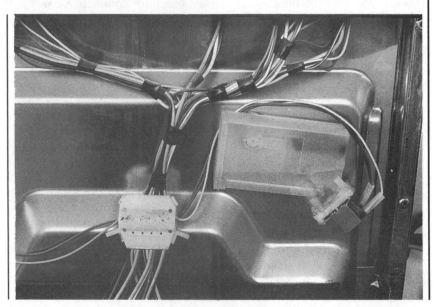

Harness connector block and support. Again, any loose connectors will overheat and cause problems. Ensure a secure fit.

Door shown with outer cover removed. The entry and exit point of the wiring harness (arrowed) on a machine with door-mounted timers and switches is prone to break faults due to the constant flexing of the wiring. Check carefully all wiring at this point and renew completely if suspect. Also ensure that all protective guards and insulators are sound and refitted correctly.

The entry point and protective covering differ from make to make. It is essential for both safety and correct running of the machine that all wiring and insulation at this point are as original.

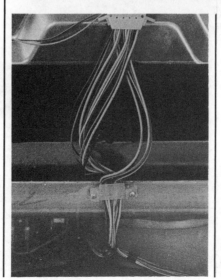

This close-up of the entry/exit point of the harness highlights the point of failure due to the constant flexing of the wiring when the door is opened and closed during use. Check this area thoroughly for any defects or poorly fitting cable protectors such as this.

Chapter 33

Useful tips and information

Shown above in the centre are the various types of clips in common use in today's machines. In the centre are the screw type wire clips. Top right is the new type toothed clip. This new clip is much easier and quicker to fit as grips or pliers are used to tighten jaws together. Left are two types of corbin spring clips. Care should be taken in removing this type of clip as they have a tendency to 'spring' – even under tension. For removal, corbin pliers are best, but ordinary grips can be used with care. Lower right is a worm drive or jubilee clip. This again is a simple but effective clip. Some machines may come with crimp type clips which are factory fitted and not reusable. Prise them loose carefully and renew them with worm drive type clips.

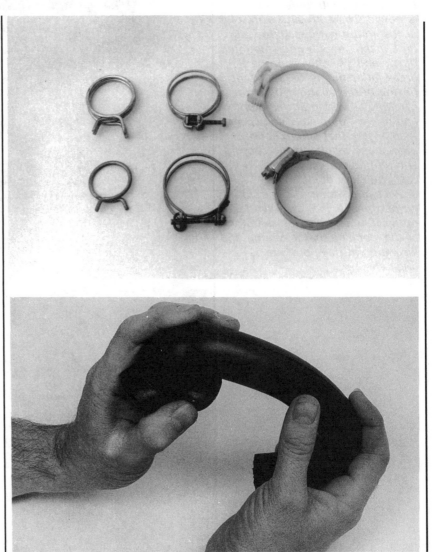

Check all hoses thoroughly for perishing and/or cracking. As with this pressure hose supplying the top spray arm, stretch the hose to enable a thorough check. (It is wise to check any new hoses before fitting).

Keep the detergent powder dry as it tends to absorb dampness from the air and form lumps that will impair the powder's performance. Use the fasteners provided in the box to re-seal the plastic bag after use.

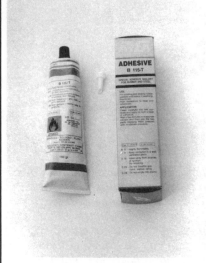

A sealant like the one shown should be used when fitting thermostat grommets, new hoses and door seals.

How it should look on a similar machine without rail bolt leak.

Some machines secure the basket rails with screws or bolts. Check these have not worked loose as the cabinet, sprayed with water during the wash can be the cause of a very difficult leak to locate. (This Philips requires the removal of the side panel to gain access to the nut on the fixing bolts). This machine had leaked for some time and several engineers had failed to locate the true fault, blaming door seals etc.

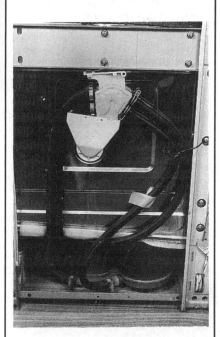

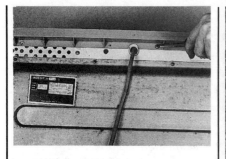

To gain access to the timer and door switch on this model, make sure the machine is totally isolated before removing the screws from the back rail.

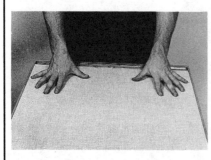

Then slide the inner of the top backwards. This may be difficult if it has not been removed before.

Smear edges with liquid soap prior to refitting. This will aid refitting and subsequent removal at a later date.

Odours or unsightly marks to the load cabinet caused by incorrect use can be alleviated by using a special dishwasher cleaner like the one shown. Read the instructions carefully before use.

When removing door panels for servicing, it is wise to counter-balance the door. If not, when the panel is removed, the doors own spring counter-balance will slam the door shut.

To avoid problems with cleaning, use a good quality detergent and rinse aid.

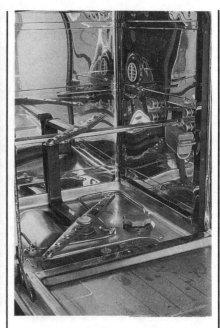

If a machine is looked after correctly and only the correct powder salt and rinse aid are used, the machine will look as good as new for years. The machine shown above is six and a half years old and is in constant use for a family of four. Note – no scaling or deposits on the interior.

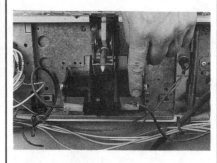

Look carefully at all connections no matter what the original fault. This was not the reason for the failure of the dispenser but if left it could be dangerous and will certainly fail in the near future. Prevention is always better than cure.

Chapter 34

Buying spare parts

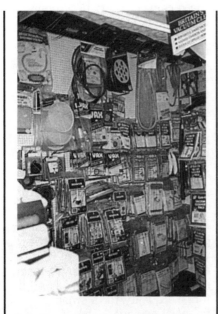

Small specialist electrical shops can offer a wide selection of spare parts.

This small but well stocked shop offers an extremely wide variety of items. Try to locate a similar shop in your own area prior to faults arising. This will save time later on.

The aim of this manual has been to assist in the DIY repair of your dishwasher. I hope that you will now not only possess a greater knowledge of how your appliance works, but also the knowledge to prevent faults from occurring.

Above all, I hope that, armed with this information, you will feel confident enough to tackle most (if not all) of the faults that may arise with your appliance from time to time.

All of this knowledge and new found confidence will, however, be wasted if you cannot locate the parts that you require to complete the repair.

In the past this would have been somewhat of a problem, but in recent years the availability of spares has increased. This is for several reasons.

1. The reluctance of people to pay high labour charges for jobs that they feel they can do themselves.
2. The general interest in household DIY coupled with the saving from call-out and labour charges, gives a feeling

of satisfaction when the job is finally complete.

3. The growth in size and number of DIY stores in recent years.
4. The improvement in the availability of pre-packed spares for many products.

In the past, many companies have been reluctant to supply parts for the DIY market, but the current trend is to expand the amount of pre-packed spares available to the public. The range of off-the-shelf spare parts in both retail outlets and mail order companies is most welcome, and many appliance manufacturers who do not have local dealerships will supply parts by post if requested. (Unfortunately this can sometimes be a long process.)

By far the best approach to obtaining the parts you require is to find a local 'spares and repairs' dealer through the yellow pages or local press. This is best done before your appliance breaks down; you will then not waste time when a fault arises. In many instances you may possess more knowledge of your machine than the assistant in the shop, so it is essential to take the MAKE, MODEL and SERIAL NUMBER of your appliance with you to help them locate or order the correct spare part for your needs.

It is always advantageous to take the faulty part with you whenever possible, to confirm visually that it is the correct replacement. It may look the same from memory, although quite substantial differences may be seen if the faulty item is compared with the newly offered item. The case or mounting plate, etc., could be different.

Pattern parts

Certain parts that are widely available are marked 'suitable for' or 'to fit'. These are generally called pattern or patent parts. Such terms refer to items or parts that are not supplied by the manufacturer of your appliance, but are designed to fit it.

Some are copies of genuine parts and others are supplied by the original parts manufacturer to an independent distributor and are then supplied to the retailer and sold to the customer. This avoids the original manufacturer's mark-up because it is not an 'official' or 'genuine' spare part. This saving is then passed onto the customer.

Many of the appliance manufacturers disliked this procedure in the past as the parts were of an inferior quality.

This, however, is not the case today because the supply of parts is very big business and quality has improved dramatically. Although great savings can be made, care must be taken not to save money by buying inferior spare parts. Check the quality of the item first wherever possible.

A reputable dealer should supply only good quality pattern or genuine parts.

Many of the original appliance manufacturers are now discounting their genuine authorised spares to combat the growth in patterned spares. This is very good, as it can only benefit you, the consumer.

Genuine parts

Parts supplied by the manufacturer of your appliance, or by their authorised local agent, are classed as genuine and will in many cases carry the companies' trade mark or colours, etc. Many of the parts in today's appliances are not in fact produced by the manufacturer of the finished items, but a subcontractor who also may supply a distributor of patterned spares with identical items.

Patterned spares producers will only take on items that have high volume sales and leave the slow moving items to the original manufacturer of the appliance. It is this that angers the manufacturer. Generally it is a long procedure to obtain spares 'direct' from the manufacturer as many are unwilling to supply small orders direct to the public. Another system used to deter small orders is to use a 'pro-forma' invoicing sheet that will delay the receipt of parts until your cheque has cleared.

With the increase in DIY, manufacturers are slowly changing their view regarding spares supply. This is simply to fend off the patterned spares, by making the original parts more available and competitively priced. Again this will in turn benefit the consumer.

In conclusion

In the end, the decision between genuine or patterned spares is yours. Cost and speed of availability may have to be taken into consideration, but do not forsake quality for a small financial saving.

As a guide a list of U.K. telephone numbers or means of contact has been compiled for the more popular brand names. The numbers shown are correct at the time of going to print, but may be subject to alteration. Information on names that do not appear in the list may often be found in your local yellow pages.

Make	Telephone No.
AEG	0753 872325
Ariston	0322 526933 (or see Yellow Pages under Merloni Domestic Appliances)
Asko (was Asea)	081 568 4666
Bauknecht	0345 898989
Bendix	Yellow Pages
Bosch	081 573 6789
Candy	051 334 2781
Colston	see Ariston (above)
Creda	Yellow Pages
Electra	see Local Electricity Board
Electrolux	0325 300660
Fagor	0707 377877
Frigidaire	051 355 0588
Hotpoint	Local Directory
Hoover	Yellow Pages
Indesit	0322 526933 (or see Yellow Pages under Merloni Domestic Appliances)
Kelvinator	051 334 2781
Miele	Yellow Pages
Philco	081 902 9626
Philips (now Whirlpool)	0345 898989
Servis	021 526 3199
Whirlpool (was Philips)	0345 898989
Zanussi	Yellow Pages/Local Directory
Zerowatt	051 334 2781

The above telephone numbers were correct at the time of publication. Changes will inevitably occur during the life span of this book.

Chapter 35

Common causes of poor washing results

Poor washing can be due to the incorrect operation of the machine by the user, or by a mechanical or electrical fault of the machine. The most common user faults are listed below.

1 Mis-use of the controls:
a) To achieve good consistent results from your dishwasher, you must have a good understanding of your machine and its controls. Always remember – YOU tell the machine what to do. If in doubt, read the manufacturer's manual.
b) Does the selected programme have the right water temperature and wash time for the load?

2 Incorrect dosage:
(a) The amount of powder/detergent that you should use is usually displayed on the side of the pack. Please remember that this is only a guide, and the amounts have to be adjusted to load size, type and degree of soiling, and the 'hardness' of the water supply.

3 Water supply:
Washing powder is formulated to do several tasks.
(a) Break the surface tension of the water.
(b) Remove the soiling from the load.
(c) Hold the soiling in suspension.
(d) Cleanse safely the wash load.

4. Incorrect loading:
(a) Overloading the washer will result in poor spray pattern within the compartment, resulting in inadequate soil removal
(b) Some programmes are for reduced loads. If one of these programmes is used, reduce the load. If you are not sure, read the manufacturer's manual.

5 Other factors:
(a) How old is the machine? Like any purchase, a dishwasher has a restricted lifespan. In the case of an automatic dish washer, the average lifespan is approximately eight years.
(b) When was the machine last serviced?
(c) Failure to check or refill salt container often enough.
(d) Failure to check or refill rinse aid dispenser at regular intervals, or adjust dosage control (if fitted).

Here in detail are some of the common and not so common causes of poor wash results. It should be remembered however, that most problems arise after a long period of time and possibly for a variety of reasons most of which are described in the following text.

Although the detection and cure of most of the faults listed will be relatively quick and easy, do not expect immediate results. In some instances, it takes several washes before an improvement is noticable on crockery, etc., depending on the length of time the problem has been allowed to build up, e.g. incorrect washing programme or incorrect powder dosage, etc.

General poor washing of crockery can often be seen as a thin layer of food left on the surface of plates, etc., or by a film of a starch-like substance. This can be felt as a rough coating if you pass a finger over the surface and will show up clearly if a cloth dipped in iodine is wiped over the surface. Such build-ups and coatings are caused by:
(a) The failure to remove surplus food from crockery prior to loading the machine. Items that have burnt on food etc., should be pre-soaked. If

items are to be left for sometime in the machine prior to a full wash cycle, it is recommended that a pre-wash is used prior to the main wash.

(b) If wash quality is poor and steps in 'a' are normally carried out, the spray arms should be checked for blockages of the jets and if necessary, cleaned. Also check for free rotation of the spray arms as it is possible that they could split along the joints or seams, therefore the pressure is lost resulting in poor washing. Check thoroughly and renew if suspect.

c) Poor loading of the machine can result in inadequate water dispersal within the cabinet and giving a poor wash. Always load the machine with care, paying particular attention not to cause any obstruction to the spray arms and if possible, leave some empty places to allow good water circulation within the machine. (Never overload your machine).

d) Check that all filters are cleaned regularly and that food deposits are not allowed to build up on them. Ensure also, that the filters are correctly positioned, otherwise food particles will be circulated during the wash cycle. A kinked or restricted outlet hose will give similar results owing to failure to discharge soiled water from the machine.

e) If a "sand-like" deposit is detected on items such as glasses or on cups that have been washed on the upper basket, the probable reason for this could be the top spray arm not rotating correctly.

Check:

1 that large items stacked on the lower basket are not obstructing the upper spray arm.

2 that the upper spray arm is not blocked or split.

3 that your dishwasher is the type that feeds the upper spray arm by an open jet from the centre of the lower arm, ensure that any large items on the lower basket do not obstruct or cover the two openings.

4 the filter. If the sump is blocked, it will reduce the circulation pump supply and in turn reduce top spray arm power.

5 that adequate detergent was used for that particular wash. **Note: under dosing can cause over foaming that greatly reduces circulation pressure. If in doubt, add more – too little detergent causes over foaming.**

f) If you are satisfied that steps have been carried out correctly, ask yourself whether the correct wash cycle was selected to combat the amount of soiling on the dishes. A wash that is either too cool in temperature or too short a cycle, can result in a poor wash. If you feel the wash programme you selected was the correct one and that all the previous points are satisfactory, then the next step is to check the thermostat as described in the *thermostat* section.

g) If sufficient detergent is used for a wash programme, the particles of food and soiling from the dishes will be unable to remain in suspension in the water long enough to be pumped away, resulting in a uniform soiling of the wash load and over a period of washes, a marked deterioration will be seen. Remember – too much detergent will do no harm, whereas too little does. Extra soiled dishes require extra detergent.

h) Faulty drying of the wash load may be caused by the following:

1 Insufficient rinse aid being dispensed at the end of the wash. This will result in lines or streaks on the clean dishes. See chapter on *Rinse aid dispensers*.

2 No rinse aid being dispensed will result in poor drying of wash load and is often accompanied by spotting on clean items. Check that the rinse aid tank is full and if it is full but not dispensing the rinse aid, refer to chapter on *Rinse aid dispensers*.

3 Too much rinse aid dispensed at the end of a wash cycle will leave smear marks and a greasy feeling to the dishes. For faults 1 to 3 check the rinse aid setting dial (if fitted) and adjust accordingly. The best results are obtained by setting the adjuster below the mid point on its scale and increasing slightly if required. Check by holding a washed plate in a horizontal position, in a way that it will catch the light, at eye level. The plate should have an overall even shine and should not be greasy or sticky to the touch. Adjust as required.

4 Drying of the wash load will be adversely affected if the door is opened too soon after the end of the programme. When the machine switches off at the end of the programme, time should be allowed for the warm air inside the machine to dry the dishes before opening the door. Once the door has been opened, the warm air escapes thus impairing the drying.

Quick trouble shooting guide

(Please read *Common Causes of Poor Wash Results* and *Discoloration Problems* along with this section)

Too much foam in the wash solution
The detergent dosage must be increased.

White spots, streaks or film on dishware
Use correct dosage of high density product, such as SUN. Use a good rinse aid, for example SUN rinse aid.

Tarnishing/rusting of stainless steel
Do not leave covered with salt or acid foodstuffs, use rinse and hold cycle. Do not wash in contact with silver – use separate cutlery baskets. Do not leave in a damp dishwasher for long periods – drying by hand is best. Wash with a good product. Use correct grade of salt in softener.

Tarnishing of silverware
Do not leave covered with salt or acid foodstuffs, use rinse and hold cycles. Do not allow undissolved product to come in contact with silver, otherwise black spots occur. Keep silver separate from other metals. Wash with a good product containing tarnish inhibitor. Use correct grade of salt in softener.

Tarnishing of Aluminium
Usually caused by hot water – tarnish is not injurious in any way, but is unsightly. Remove article before hot final rinse.

Poor results
Check filters.
Check spray arms.
Check detergent dosage.
Check water softener (if fitted).
Check water temperature.

Poor drying
Check rinse aid dispenser.
Check air vent in machine is free.
Check water is fully drained.
Check stacking of items.

Noise
Can be a problem with some machines – ensure correct placement of machine.

Crystal Glass
Susceptible to damage with hot water – do not wash in a dishwasher.

On glaze decorations
Some, especially antiques, are not safe in a dishwasher. Always use a good product designed for domestic use. Wash a sample piece of suspect ware for a few weeks to check suitability, short washing cycles and lower temperatures will help keep decorations brighter.

Handles
Some glued on handles will not be safe at high temperatures.
Bone, wood or plastic can be susceptible to damage by hot water. Test wash one piece for a few weeks.

Coloured Aluminium
Colour can be removed by hot alkali – do not wash in a dishwasher.

Plastics
Thermosetting plastics can dull or crack in hot water. Thermoplastics can melt – special care may be needed. Do not force into positions on racks. This will cause distortion of item.

Glass
Stack carefully to avoid rubbing and jamming.
Excessively softened water can attack glass. Do not use machine softener if water is already soft.

Handles
Pieces of cutlery produced from two types of metal are susceptible to electrolytic corrosion. Knives produced with stainless steel blades and silver handles can corrode if left in the dishwasher.

Discoloration problems

There are several reasons why discoloration may occur in your dishwasher. Some are a direct result of chemical actions, others are often caused by misuse. Often things are not dishwasher proof such as items with patterns on top of a protective glaze (check by close inspection of item), or the mixing of cutlery of different metals in the same basket, may have been loaded in the machine. What follows is a guide to the more common and not so common problems, their causes and, where possible the remedies.

Problem 1

Crockery washed in the machine is acquiring a white coating and the inside of the machine is also acquiring the same white coating (even on stainless steel lined machines).

The normal detergent and wash action of the machine break down the food particles on the wash load. These combine with any calcium salts present in the water to form a water soluble compound that is held in suspension in the water, ready to be discharged by the outlet pump. Insufficient detergent will result in the water no longer being able to hold such compounds in suspension. Such unstable compounds of calcium will then coat the wash load and interior of the machine. This may be a gradual process as some of the compounds will be discharged depending on the lack of detergent.

Similar problems can occur if the water softener unit fails or is not replenished with salt often enough. See chapter *Internal water softeners*. If your machine does not have a built in water softener, ensure adequate use of detergent, but if the problem persists, it may be wise to fit a softener kit to your machine.

Calcium build-up maybe removed or at least reduced depending on how long the problem has been allowed to continue. Your local chemist should be able to supply you with a citric acid powder for this purpose. Load the machine with the crockery to be treated and use 100 grams (3.05 oz.) of this white and very acidic powder in place of the usual detergent. If the dispenser will not take the full amount, the surplus can be put on the lower section of the door before closing, or alternatively, sprinkle in the load compartment. Select a normal wash cycle and allow the machine to operate normally. It would be wise to stop the machine mid cycle to make sure the powder has been fully dispensed. The action of the acid wash should remove the calcium (alkaline) build-up, although in severe cases, more than one wash may be required.

As with all chemicals both normal detergent powders and the citric acid powder, care should be taken when used, and should always be kept out of the way of children.

Problem 2

A similar white deposit or coating on the wash load may be found which gives the crockery, and especially glassware, a salty taste. As this taste implies, the fault lies in a build up of salt, and is not a calcium problem as previously described.

The causes of these salt coatings are usually the result of a poorly fitting salt cap or seal, or a small hairline type crack in the cap especially if the cap combines a level indicator. Inspect closely and renew if in doubt. Always ensure that the salt container top is correctly and securely fitted and that the seal is in good condition.

If the fault persists when the cap and seal have been checked, the regeneration system or valve could prove to be faulty although this is very unusual. The deposit will clear slowly on normal washes once the source of the problem is rectified.

Problem 3

White crockery turning pink. This can happen for a variety of reasons, the main one being the crockery itself not being dishwasher proof. The pink colour is formed by a chemical reaction by the powder used in the dishwasher on the unprotected surface of the crockery. This discoloration is irreversible.

If the "pinkish tinge" is appearing on crockery that IS dishwasher proof, the most likely cause is under dosing (using too little detergent). Under dosing allows a silicate film to form on the items which in turn absorbs iron and manganese particles from the water resulting in a brown discoloration or a pink tinge or bloom.

Iron and manganese are present in all water supplies and their presence is quite normal until under dosing occurs which enables them to adhere to the surface of crockery. A return to correct dosage of powder will, over a period of washes, greatly improve the appearance of such stained items.

Problem 4

Tarnishing of metal ware and cutlery. There are a great variety of metals used for cutlery and cooking utensils from silver and silver plate (E.P.N.S.) through to aluminium and bronze, and not all metals or the utensils made from them are dishwasher proof. Check when purchasing such items whenever possible. If you are unsure, here are a few points to watch for:

a) When loading your machine, do not combine cutlery of different metals as electro-chemical reactions may occur between them which could result in discoloration and/or pitting of the surface.

b) Make sure the correct amount of rinse aid is dispensed. Even stainless steel is susceptible to slight tarnishing if water is allowed to remain on it until it evaporates. It is perhaps wise to remove stainless steel items from the machine as soon as possible after the drying cycle as the humid atmosphere can impair the stainless properties. Note: Stainless steel surfaces require the healing effect of oxygen from the atmosphere for its protective coating. Foods containing acids, e.g. vinegar or fruit juices, table salt etc., can also penetrate the protective coating of stainless steel if allowed to remain for too long on its surface. All these problems are more pronounced on inferior grades of stainless steel, a more prominent feature of which is pitting and rust marks or circles appearing on the surface. These are caused by iron particles within the item rusting. Pitting can also occur if the stainless steel item was poorly finished on production. The surface effect of stainless steel is achieved by highly polishing, but poor finishing obviously results in poor stainless steel.

Bronze or bronze plated items should not be washed in a dishwasher as it is prone to rapid tarnishing. Any such items should be washed by hand and dried immediately.

Nickel silver, sometimes called "German Silver" is an alloy and prone to acquiring a yellow tinge if washed in a dishwasher. This type of silver requires frequent polishing to keep in peak condition and washing by hand is recommended.

Solid silver and electro plated nickel silver (E.P.N.S.) tarnish easily, even under normal conditions and require regular cleaning to keep them attractive. Items made of this silver can be washed in a dishwasher, and some manufacturers supply as an extra, a special basket for silver or E.P.N.S items. This basket will remove the tarnishing on the items whilst the machine cleans off the normal soiling. This process is electrolytical between the basket and the cutlery. A special point to note is that if the plating on any E.P.N.S. item has worn through to expose the base metal, do not put it in the special silver basket, but wash it separately.

Problem 5

Discoloration or tarnishing of polished aluminium pots and pans can occur due to the high alkalinity of the wash water and certain minerals that it may contain. If such items are removed prior to the last heated rinse, further discoloration will be avoided.

Painted or coloured aluminium articles sometimes discolour for the same reason, so if you want to keep their bright appearance, wash them by hand.

Problem 6

The inside of the cabinet appears to be going rusty in places. Rust marks appear for several reasons. Some early machines had a plastic coating over the ordinary steel shell, but once the coating had chipped or flaked, the exposed metal rusted quickly because of the harsh environment within the cabinet. A coating of an epoxy resin over the rusted areas should help, but remember to clean the area thoroughly first and follow the resin manufacturer's instructions for mixing and drying times, etc.

Rust marks may also appear on stainless steel linings, but as the stainless steel used in manufacture is generally of the finest grade and therefore suited to the job, the rust marks will be the result of external nuts or clamps (made of ordinary mild steel) used for securing thermostats or heaters, etc. These marks may then migrate along the surface of the stainless steel at or around such points.

Check and cure the leak, renewing any badly corroded items to prevent further markings. The rust stains can easily be removed by using a cleaner, e.g. 3 in 1 Chrome Cleaner or Solvol Autosol or any similar product.

If the plastic coating is chipped or flaked from the load baskets, rust marks will appear. Again, this could be remedied by using an epoxy resin, but in severe cases, it may be as well to renew the baskets. Although the baskets are relatively tough, do take care when loading them with sharp items.

Problem 7

Damaged crockery and glasses. Modern dishwashers will rarely cause breakages or chipping. The more usual cause of damage is due to items being knocked during normal use forming small unseen cracks which absorb water when washed. The subsequent heating and cooling of the water within the crack first expands and then contracts resulting in a larger, more obvious crack or chip to flake off during the cycle. Overloading can also contribute to this problem as not enough room is allowed for the items to expand during the heating process.

Similar problems occur with glass, but the cause is generally "ring structures" formed in the glass during manufacture due to stress within the glass. This allows particles within the glass to be etched away by the hot water used during the wash and last rinse. Washing by hand would eventually give the same result, although it would take much longer because of the lower water temperature and the less aggressive detergent action.

Houses with full size domestic water softeners may encounter similar problems such as etchings or cloudiness forming on the glass surface. Water that is softened 100% could have this effect on glass. It may be beneficial to contact the softener suppliers and arrange a bypass to be fitted to allow 5 degrees of hardness through to the house supply.

Chapter 36

Symbols and their meanings

A growing trend in all areas is the use of symbols to indicate the setting and operation, not only of dishwashers but washing machines, fridges, cars, etc. Such symbols are used to transcend language barriers as the symbol conveys the same message in any language.

Not all the symbols used have obvious meaning and sometimes alternatives may be used. Shown are some of those that are likely to be found on dishwashers and their meanings.

1   Intensive or heavy wash for heavily soiled items.

2   Intensive normal wash

3   Normal wash

4   Economic wash

5   Delicate

6   Rinses or pre-rinses

7   Rinsing with rinse aid

8   Drying (heated)

9   Economy wash

10 Salt indication

Chapter 37

Jargon

Armature	Wire wound centre of brush motor.
Bi-metal	Two different metals which have been joined together. When heated the strip bends in a known direction.
Burn-out	Overheated part of item.
Carbon face (seal)	Watertight flat surface seal.
Ceramic seal	Watertight flat surface seal.
Closed circuit	A normal circuit that allows power to pass through.
Contact	Point at which switch makes contact.
Continuity	Electrical path with no break.
Component	Individual parts of the machine, i.e., pump, valves, motor are all components.
Corbin	Type of spring hose clip.
Cycle	Programme or operation time.
Dispenser	Compartment that takes washing powder/liquid.
Drift	Soft metal rod used for bearing removal.
Door seal	Watertight seal for door.
Early	Machine not currently on the market.
Earth loop test	Means of determining resistance of earth path.
Energize (Energise)	To supply power to.
Energized (Energised)	Having power supplied to.
E.L.C.B.	Earth leakage circuit breaker – see *R.C.C.B.*
Flowchart	Method of following complicated steps in a logical fashion.
Functional test	To test machine on a set programme.
Grommet fitting	Method of fitting hoses etc., whilst requiring no clips.
Harness	Electrical wiring within a machine.
Hertz	Periodic cycle of one second, i.e., cycles per second.
'Hunting'	Oscillating.
I.E.E.	Institute of Electrical Engineers.
Impeller	The blades of the pump that pumps the water.
Insulation	Material used to insulate a device or a region.
Isolate	To disconnect from the electricity supply and water supply, etc.
Laminations	Joined metal parts of stator.
Late	Current machine on market.
Make	1. Manufacturer's name.
	2. When a switch makes contact it is said to 'make'.
Open-circuit	Circuit that is broken, i.e., will not let any power through.
Porous	Item that allows water to pass through.
Programmer	See *Timers (Programmers)*

P.S.I.	Measurement of water pressure, pounds per square inch, i.e. 138 p.s.i.
R.C.C.B.	Residual current circuit breaker (also know as R.C.D.)
Regeneration	Restoration of resin granules with salt.
Rotor	Central part of an induction motor.
Schematic diagram	Theoretical diagram.
Seal	Piece of pre-shaped rubber that usually fits into a purpose-built groove, therefore creating a watertight seal.
Sealant	Rubber substance used for ensuring watertight joints.
Shell	Outer of machine.
Spades	Connections on wires or components that can be pulled off gently.
Stat	Thermostat.
Stator	Electrical winding on motor.
Suspension	A dispersion of solid or liquid particles in fluid.
Syphon	A way of emptying the machine via gravity.
Terminal block	A method of connecting wires together safely.
Timer	Programme switch.
T.O.C.	Thermal overload cut-out. At a pre-set temperature, the T.O.C. will break electrical circuit to whatever it is attached, i.e., prevents motors, etc., overheating.

AT HOME IN WORLD WAR TWO

AT WORK

Stewart Ross

Evans Brothers Limited

ie motor cyclist messenger, roaring across country from
Headquarters to scattered units is now an ATS girl

Published by Evans Brothers Limited
2A Portman Mansions
Chiltern Street
London W1U 6NR

© White-Thomson Publishing Limited 2004

Produced for Evans Brothers Limited by White-Thomson Publishing Ltd
2/3 St Andrew's Place, Lewes, East Sussex BN7 1UP

Printed in Dubai

Editor: Philippa Smith/Steve White-Thomson
Consultant and Picture Researcher: Terry Charman, Historian,
    Research and Information Department, Imperial War Museum
Designer: Christopher Halls, Mind's Eye Design Ltd, Lewes
Proofreader: Philippa Smith

British Library Cataloguing in Publication Data
Ross, Stewart
    At work. - (At home in World War Two)
    1. World War, 1939-1945 - War work - Great Britain - Juvenile literature
    2. World War, 1939-1945 - Women - Great Britain - Juvenile literature
    3. Labor - Great Britain - History - 20th century - Juvenile literature
    I. Title
    941'. 084

ISBN 0237525836

Captions:
Cover and this page: ATS (Auxiliary Territorial Service) poster showing a woman
motorcycle messenger.
Cover (centre): Training on lathes given to young men in a Royal Ordnance Factory.
Cover (background): An aircraft production factory in full swing.
Title page: Part of the Government's massive drive to construct more bomber aircraft
with which to strike back at the enemy.
Contents page: A woman working for the dairy industry, on her milk round.

For sources of quoted material see page 31.

CONTENTS

TOTAL WAR

During World War Two (1939-45) the British people worked as they had never done before. Millions did voluntary tasks. Many others, especially women, did paid jobs for the first time in their lives. Unlike in peace time, the Government could tell people what work they had to do. As a result, men and women found themselves doing jobs they had never even dreamed of, such as building and driving tanks, and fighting fires.

◀ *Women engineers repair an aircraft. Few women did this type of work before the war.*

Britain joined World War Two on the side of France, Belgium, the Netherlands, Poland and other countries. They fought against Germany and, later, Italy. In 1941, Russia and the USA joined the war on Britain's side, forming the Allies, and Japan sided with Germany and Italy. The fighting spread right around the world. The war finally ended with an Allied victory in 1945.

▶ *A dramatic government poster stresses the importance of factory work in helping to win the war.*

The new Airborne Army is now in action in Europe—equipped by British factories.

THE ATTACK BEGINS IN THE FACTORY

World War Two was a 'total' war, meaning the warring countries did everything possible to win – even bombing civilians. The British Government needed every person, every factory and every field for the war effort – only if the whole country pulled together could victory be achieved.

THE PATH TO WAR

Adolf Hitler became leader of Germany in 1933. Backed by his Nazi Party, he removed those who opposed him and began taking over neighbouring countries. After Germany took over Czechoslovakia, Britain and France promised to support anyone else threatened by Nazi aggression. On 1 September 1939, Hitler invaded Poland. Two days later, Britain and France declared war on Germany.

◀ *Pensioners come out of retirement to work on a tank. Everyone – young and old – was urged to pull together to ensure victory.*

Over 4 million men and women were conscripted into the armed forces: the army, navy and air force. Others were directed to jobs like making weapons (see page 17) and working on secret codes (see page 19). Before the war unemployment had been a serious problem, with about 1.5 million people out of a job at the beginning of 1939. By 1943 it had disappeared – in fact, there were not enough people to do the work needed.

▶ *Posters like this encouraging people to get involved in war work, were a common sight in London and other big cities.*

COME ON – HELP BUILD US PLANES, GUNS AND SHIPS MOBILISE FOR WAR WORK

GOVERNMENT ORDERS

THE NATION NEEDS
TRAINED MEN

MINISTRY OF LABOUR
AND NATIONAL SERVICE

▲ A poster stresses the need for trained men to work in the factories contributing to the war effort.

The Government, headed by the prime minister, had the task of directing war work. In 1939 the prime minister was Neville Chamberlain. In May 1940 he was replaced by the 65-year-old Winston Churchill. An inspiring leader, he worked with a small group of ministers called his 'war cabinet'.

Several ministers were responsible for work. Of these, the most important was Ernest Bevin, a brilliant former trades union leader who understood the needs and hopes of ordinary working people. He was Minister of Labour and National Service.

New laws (known as 'Acts'), such as the Emergency Powers Act and the Control of Employment Act (both 1939), gave the Government sweeping powers over people's lives. In 1943, for example, Bevin ordered some young army recruits to become coal miners instead of soldiers. By the following year, as well as those who had been conscripted into the armed forces, more than a million others were in jobs they had been told to do.

▼ These young conscripts ('Bevin Boys') were sent to work as miners rather than into the armed forces (1943).

By and large, these measures were not unpopular. Fighting for its life, the country trusted Churchill to do what was needed for victory. Indeed, too many people volunteered for war work in the armed forces, the Civil Defence and jobs in industry.

To deal with this problem, lists were made of 'reserved occupations'. These were key jobs in areas like engineering, agriculture and medicine that people were not allowed leave to do something else.

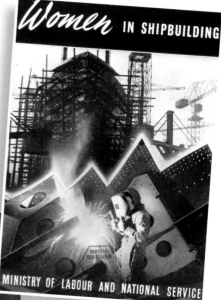

▲ A poster encourages women to work in shipyards.

◄ Factory work, in this case filing metal on a vice, could be boring, but it was quite well paid.

'Marion Finds A Fighting Job Too
When Marion's boyfriend was called up, she wanted to be in it too. So she asked at the employment exchange about war work . . . In next to no time they had fixed her up at a Government Training Centre, learning to make munitions . . . And before long she was in an important job. At last she felt she was really "doing her bit" . . .'

A government advertisement that many women found rather childish

'Accept War Job or You Lose Your Dole – From today onwards a man who refuses a job of national importance because it offers less money than his old job will be punished by having his unemployment benefit stopped for six weeks.'

Daily Express,
15 July 1940

EMERGENCY SERVICES

To cope with the effects of enemy bombing, the Government set up Air Raid Precautions, later renamed Civil Defence. More than 1.25 million people joined, working for Air Raid Precautions (ARP), and the fire, rescue and ambulance services. In 1942 the Government said that Civil Defence workers had to be prepared to work in any branch of the service. The punishment for refusing might be a month in prison. Even stricter, the next year everyone had to 'volunteer' for unpaid Civil Defence work!

▲ Rescue workers after a tough night on duty. 'SP' stood for 'Stretcher Party'.

The fire service was hardest pressed. In 1939 there were only about 6,000 firefighters and 1,850 water pumps for the whole country. New recruits, men and women, formed the Auxiliary Fire Service (AFS) of 36,000 full-timers and

◀ Using appliances floating on the River Thames, London's firefighters tackle fires caused by enemy bombing.

many hundreds of thousands of part-timers and unpaid volunteers. Of these, 47,000 were women. Battling with the enormous fires that raged in bombed cities was the toughest war work on the home front. About 800 firefighters were killed and some 7,000 seriously injured.

Ambulance and first-aid work was often sad. The worst job was collecting the bodies of air-raid victims. Rescue work could be both tragic and uplifting. One London woman, whose mother, sister and child had been killed, was rescued after being trapped in a bombed house for almost five days.

A full-time police war reserve was called up and joined by large numbers of part-time special constables. The police did all kinds of extra work, such as air-raid shelter duty and checking on suspicious foreigners.

Women! You are needed in THE NATIONAL FIRE SERVICE AS FULL-TIME OR PART-TIME MEMBERS

You can train to be a telephonist, despatch rider, driver, canteen worker and for many other duties.

▲ This poster urges women to join the National Fire Service.

'Every Saturday night and often on Thursdays I couldn't get home because I was driving an ambulance. I used to go to the old police station in Ness and sleep in the cells.'

May Lawton

◀ Rescue workers lift an injured woman from the wreckage of her bombed home.

ARP WORKERS

▲ A 1939 recruitment poster for the ARP (Air Raid Precautions).

▼ ARP workers sit with their gas masks on, ready to go to people's help during a raid.

The Government began setting up Air Raid Precautions in 1935. By 1939 it had built air-raid shelters, issued gas masks (in case of attack by poisonous gas) and recruited thousands of ARP workers. One of these was Helen Robertson from Glasgow:

'I saw an advert in the local paper for volunteers to do air-raid duties, so myself and my husband Jimmy both joined as wardens.

I was part-time to begin with then went full-time, working with the fire and ambulance people. We were given navy blue overalls, a whistle and a white tin hat with 'ARP' in black letters on the front. Most of the time I just walked about at night making sure people didn't have any lights showing from the outside. The worst time was when we got blitzed, the Clydebank Blitz – 13th and 14th March 1941 it was. I was too busy to be frightened but I was glad to be alive at the end. I remember being worried about our minister's wife alone in her big house, so I went and took her and her husband to a shelter. Later, their house got a direct hit.'

Helen and her husband were ARP wardens. Their duties included checking that houses were blacked out, leading people to shelters when air-raid warnings sounded, and helping with rescue work after a raid. Most wardens were volunteers. A nurse volunteer warden recalled the fear of walking in dark silent streets, knowing the tall buildings on either side were empty. Full-time wardens were paid £3-5s-0d (£3.25) a week, and the women £2-3s-6d (£2.17). About one in six wardens were women.

Other ARP workers included runners, mostly young boys in the Boy Scouts, who carried messages on foot or on their bikes, and fire spotters. Spotters took it in turn to sit on the roof of their office or factory at night and watch out for fire bombs. It was dangerous work and bitterly cold in the winter.

Most wardens were middle-aged or older, as this man remembered with a laugh at the time:

> 'They started off this service with the idea that it was a kind of muck heap for anyone they didn't want in the army. Can you tell me of four wardens at our post, bar you and me, who can run fifty yards without conking out?'

▲ An ARP warden checks with his chief warden before going out on patrol.

▼ ARP wardens equipped with axes and crowbars to help them break into any buildings if necessary during an air raid.

DOCTORS AND NURSES

The Government listed all jobs in order of importance to the war effort. Those at the top of the list were known as 'Priority Job no. 1'. Doctors and nurses, as well as fighter pilots, were in this category.

▼ *Recruitment posters like this emphasised the value and glamour of the job, not the low pay.*

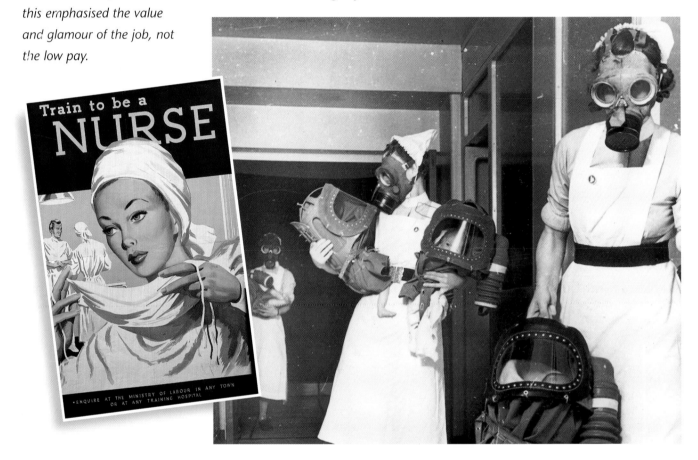

Train to be a
NURSE

•ENQUIRE AT THE MINISTRY OF LABOUR IN ANY TOWN OR AT ANY TRAINING HOSPITAL

▲ *Nurses with babies in specially-made gas masks – understandably they were terrified.*

'I suppose I was not called up to be an army dentist because I had a rather important patient. His name was Winston Churchill.'

William Stewart-Ross

From 1939–40, thousands of doctors, nurses and dentists were called up into the armed forces. This produced severe shortages in medical services for the rest of the population. By 1945 there were 33 per cent fewer General Practitioners (GPs) than in 1939. In response, medical staff had to work longer hours. Nurses, for example, often worked 10- or 12-hour shifts. Even then some of them still found the energy to do voluntary work, such as fire spotting (see page 11).

Diana Hutchinson remembers:

'I got up at five or six o'clock in the evening, went to have a meal, and then I was on duty from eight o'clock until eight the next morning. It was very hard staying awake all night, even if you had slept in the day. Four o'clock in the morning was the worst time, and if Sister came round and found you asleep she rapped your knuckles.'

Nurse Kate Phipps recalled seeing the wounded soldiers returning from France in June 1940:

'I was glad Sister had warned us about the stench of dried blood. We wanted to smile a welcome but felt nearer crying.'

Thousands of women volunteered to become nurses with the Civil Nursing Reserve, the Voluntary Aid Detachments (VAD) and the Women's Voluntary Service (WVS). They were given a much shortened training and rushed into service.

Doctors could not be trained so quickly, so many older doctors put off retirement and worked enormously long hours. During the Blitz some specialists worked on the streets all night and then returned to their hospitals, still in their steel helmets, to begin their normal work. In the middle of an air raid one surgeon was lifted on a crane to a man trapped on the top floor of a bombed-out building. He had to cut off the man's leg, there and then, to set him free.

▲ *A bombed hospital, 1940. The Government allowed this picture to be shown because it reflected badly on the enemy, but it would not allow the hospital's name to be given in case it helped the Germans assess the accuracy of their bombing.*

◄ *A doctor inspects a man injured during an air raid. Doctors on the home front were desperately overworked because so many of their colleagues were away working with the armed forces.*

13

DAD'S ARMY

To meet the threat of possible invasion, in May 1940 the
Local Defence Volunteers (LDV) were established. Volunteer
Colin Cuthbert of Kent remembers his first LDV parade:

'There was a very cosmopolitan [mixed] bunch of people of all
ages and all stages, doctors, brewers, shopkeepers, old men,
young men like myself in that day, and the Superintendent of
the Police was in charge of the parade and he asked everyone
to fall in [line up] in threes, which I did for the first time in my
life. We were told that the country was in a parlous [worrying]
state and that things were serious which we knew from what
we had seen with our own eyes coming ashore down Margate
Pier. [The defeated army returning from France.] We were going
to try and do what we could so he asked had anybody got any
guns or armaments [weapons] at all? To my surprise every man
there dived his hand under his coat and produced relics from
the First World War [1914-18] and an assortment of old guns.
These were collected and that was the beginning.'

▼ A member of the Surrey
Home Guard polishes his
submachine gun at the
dining room table.

Members of the Home Guard (Local Defence Volunteers) learn basic German in case they capture enemy soldiers.

At its peak some 1,800,000 men had joined the LDV, which became known as the Home Guard (better known today as 'Dad's Army'). It patrolled at night in case of unexpected attack by parachutists, and guarded key places like railway stations. It was finally disbanded in late 1944, when all possibility of invasion had gone.

In 1942 the women's equivalent of the Home Guard appeared, the Women's Home Defence Corps (WHDC). It was very informal, with no signing on or uniform. As Colin Cuthbert suggests, these unpaid defence forces were under-armed, poorly trained and lacked proper discipline. Nevertheless, they gave people an opportunity to 'do their bit' for their country at a time of great danger.

'We don't want to fight, but if it comes to it, we might as well know how to defend ourselves and our homes.'

A member of WHDC

Special detachments of the Home Guard – Station Guards – in training. They were established to protect the railway network and could be called in to defend vital rail links in an emergency.

FACTORY WORK

Britain was not well prepared for war in 1939. It was short of military vehicles, guns, aircraft, ships and munitions. By June 1940 the situation was even worse. The British army had been defeated in France. Although most of the men had been rescued, much of their equipment had been lost.

Under the slogan 'Go To It', the Government urged everyone to work for victory. It swapped factory production from non-essential goods like cars to military vehicles. The unemployed received government training to get back to work. The rewards could be great: by 1940, when a soldier earned 14 shillings (70p) a week (plus food and accommodation), a skilled lathe operator could earn £7.00–£8.00 a week. Employers hired 'labour scouts' to attract skilled workers by offering them higher wages.

▼ *Recycling was part of everyday life in wartime Britain, as this poster suggests. Recycled paper was used to make bomb containers.*

FROM WASTE PAPER TO MUNITIONS OF WAR

▼ *Young men train to use lathes in a Royal Ordnance Factory.*

Finally, millions of women went to work. Between 1939 and 1943 the number of women in civil jobs rose from 5,094,000 to 7,253,000.

▼ By 1943, 90 per cent of women of working age were employed.

The results were remarkable (see panel). In the first week of June 1940, industrial production rose by a staggering 25 per cent. One factory doubled its output of essential parts for fighter planes in just thirteen days.

PERCENTAGE INCREASE IN ARMAMENTS MANUFACTURE, 1939–44	
Small-arms and shells	1,000%
Guns	750%
War vehicles (excluding tanks)	350%
All aircraft	300%
Bombers	1,000%

The human cost, though, was high. Many women were paid less than £2.00 for a 60-hour week in dirty, noisy and unhealthy – even dangerous – conditions. For safety reasons, munitions factories were situated on remote sites that took hours to reach. Some employees even had to move to a different part of the country to be closer to their war work.

'Twenty-two-year-old Dora Yeoman, ex-piemaker of Newcastle, is now doing the work of three men in a Midlands munitions factory. At midnight Dora was walking in circles operating three huge machines when she told the Daily Mirror: "I never operate less than two machines at a time."'

Daily Mirror, 20 August, 1942

THE INTELLIGENCE SERVICE

▼ *Highly qualified radio communications operators were vital to the war effort.*

As war is fought with brains as well as brawn, the Government was eager to get the sharpest talent into war work. Writers like George Orwell and artists like Paul Nash helped by using their creative talents to produce writing and pictures that supported the British point of view. Other intellectuals were given jobs in the Intelligence Service. Author Mary Wesley recalls her job interview for the Intelligence Service:

> 'We talked about dairy farming for an hour. Then he said, "Right, you can start on Monday." I said, "But what am I going to do?" And he said, "Oh, you'll find out when you start."'

The Intelligence Service gathered information about the enemy. It listened to their radio broadcasts (there was no television during the war), read their newspapers and magazines, and collected information from spies and others. When the Allies were planning to invade France in the summer of 1944 (known as the 'D-Day landings'), for example, the Intelligence Service was asked to find out about the coast on which the soldiers were going to land. By collecting hundreds of holiday and other photos, it pieced together a complete picture of all the target beaches.

'I was a professor of Medieval German, so I knew the enemy's language and culture – perhaps even their way of thinking – better than almost anyone else in the country. Of course, they took me into the Intelligence Service straight away.'

Bertie Troop

▼ *Royal Air Force plotters plan operations over the Channel. The blocks on the table represented the ships, aircraft and soldiers of each side.*

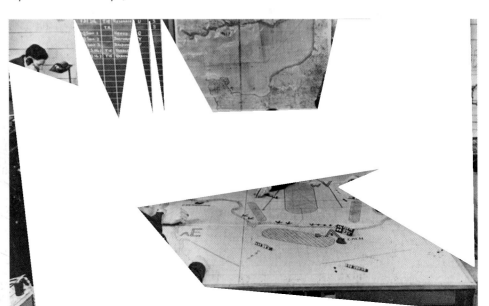

▶ *The famous German Enigma code machine that came into British hands and enabled them, unknown to the enemy, to read most of their messages.*

The Intelligence Service's greatest success was breaking Germany's secret code. German messages were translated into code by an early type of computer, known as Enigma. This was reproduced by Polish code experts just before the war, and a copy given to the British Intelligence Service.

Based in Bletchley Park, Buckinghamshire, a group of highly gifted men and women made a machine, known as 'Colossus', that deciphered the German code. The work was not made fully public until the 1990s. Even today, many who worked at Bletchley Park are not keen to talk about their top secret wartime work.

'We knew we were doing something important but because no one was allowed to talk about it, I don't think we realised just how vital it was. It was more fun than my pre-war job as a university secretary ... '

Martha McGreggor, who worked at Bletchley

▼ *The brains behind the battle – members of the 'Windy Ridge' Special Operations Group who passed on intercepted enemy messages to commanders in the front line.*

WOMEN IN WORK

▶ A Ministry of Information exhibition shows photos of the many different jobs that women did during the war to support the armed forces.

▼ A poster urging women to work as army message carriers. Most army work, however, was a great deal less exciting.

CARRY THE MESSAGES

The motor cyclist messenger, roaring across country from Headquarters to scattered units is now an ATS girl

The war gave some people the opportunity to do what they had dreamed of all their lives, people like Christina Kirby, for instance:

'I used to drive a milk cart with three churns in the back from the time I was eight. . . . When the war came . . . I wanted to drive and thought the best chance of doing this was in the ATS [Auxiliary Territorial Service, the women's branch of the army] . . . It was at Ashford [in Surrey] that I got into driving. That's where I had all the fun. The depot was huge, three miles around, nothing but vehicles in it. All sorts – tanks, and amphibious ducks that went down on the river. I'd get to the depot in the morning, and the officer there would say there's a hundred Bedfords [a type of lorry] to get ready for when the soldiers come to pick them up. I would get them petrolled, make sure the tyres were all right, move them to the place where they'd be collected, and line them up. I went from these vehicles to moving tanks, then, towards the end of the war, jeeps.'

EYES OF THE GUNS

Raiders overhead – from the predictors manned by ATS come the orders that direct the gunners

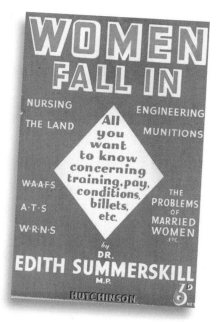

Getting a job as a driver was one of the few ways most people ever got a chance to drive during the war. The normal way of travelling was by bus or train. There were few private cars and very little petrol to put in them. It was reserved for those who needed it most, like the armed forces and emergency services.

As Christina discovered, driving at night was extremely dangerous because vehicles were allowed to show very little light and all street lights were switched off. In case they might help German invaders, all sign posts were taken down too.

▲ *The home front would have collapsed within months if women had not played as major a role as men in all war work – except actually firing guns, which they were forbidden to do!*

► *Instruction leaflets issued to the many war workers, especially single women, who were often required to work far from home.*

A *Women's World* advertisement for a lorry driver:
'*. . . some knowledge of driving is necessary to start with but after that, what you don't know you'll very soon learn, not only in the lorries but under them.*'

'CONCHIES'

'War will cease when men refuse to fight. What are YOU going to do about it?'

Peace Pledge Union poster pinned up in the summer of 1940

More than 59,000 conscientious objectors (COs or 'conchies') refused to obey the Government's orders to join the armed forces. Their action was based on their beliefs: some were pacifists who did not believe war was ever justified; others, like Quakers and Buddhists, were banned from fighting by their religious beliefs.

▶ Conscientious objectors on a march protesting against the call-up.

The Government accepted conscientious objection as long as it was genuine. COs had to prove their sincerity before a local five-person tribunal. These gave 3,577 people (including the composer Benjamin Britten) complete exemption from war service. However, 12,204 claims were turned down, and these people did not have to join the services but had to do other useful work instead. Only 3 per cent of COs were sent to prison.

Little interest was taken in COs in 1939, but in 1940, when the country was in peril, there was some hostility towards them. Their friends refused to talk to them, and thousands lost their jobs in industry and local government because their employers did not want COs working for them. Most stuck fiercely to their principles: churchman George Elphick of Lewes, Sussex, was imprisoned five times for refusing to do firewatching duty. He said he would not do any work connected with the war.

'Colonel F. Longden Smith, chief of Skipton's Fire Brigade Committee, yesterday warned conscientious objectors that they must make their own arrangements to protect their homes from incendiary [fire] bombs.'

Sunday Dispatch, 23 June 1940

COs worked as stretcher bearers, rescue workers, clerks, secretaries and fishermen. A number worked on the land with the Women's Land Army, and with 40,000 German and Italian prisoners of war. There were even 7,000 of them in the army's Non-Combatant Labour Corps.

▲ *Some conscientious objectors were prepared to take dangerous jobs, such as deep-sea fishing, as long as they did not have to carry guns.*

◀ *Young men unfit for fighting and conscientious objectors train for the army's Non-Combatant Labour Corps.*

Sport

E ven before the outbreak of war most professional sportsmen (there were almost no professional sportswomen in those days) had lost or changed their jobs. Young fit men were ideal recruits, so hundreds of footballers, cricketers and rugby league players were called up straight away.

Arsenal Football Club, which encouraged its players to join up, lost all but two of its 42 professionals. England's most talented inside forward, Raich Carter, joined the Auxiliary Fire Service. Later, after criticism from the newspapers that he was not really 'doing his bit', he signed up with the RAF.

> 'Goalkeeper Stayed off Work – Fined
> Clyde goalkeeper Gilbert McKie, who pleaded he was suffering from rheumatism, but who was able to play football on Saturdays, was fined £13 or 35 days [in prison] by Sheriff Burn-Murdoch at Stirling yesterday for being absent from work at Stirling colliery [coal mine] on 13 occasions.'
>
> *Daily Express*, 14 May 1943

▼ *All the services encouraged their personnel to take part in team sports because this kept up morale and helped them keep fit. The services' first teams contained many peacetime professionals.*

▶ *Wartime international – Belgian refugees v Dutch refugees, London, 1941.*

Many clubs closed down and league football was reorganised on a local and regional basis. The players, young men or part-timers, received only match fees. Often it was a matter of selecting whomever happened to be off duty at the time. Because of the bomb threat, crowds were limited to one-eighth (later one-quarter) of their pre-war size. Many famous sporting grounds were unplayable. Arsenal's Highbury became a Civil Defence headquarters, the rugby ground at Twickenham was an allotment patch, the Oval cricket ground was used as a prisoner-of-war camp, and Wimbledon tennis courts were a parade ground. Only six horse racing courses remained open, and races were limited to local horses.

There was still plenty of sport as the armed forces encouraged it as a way of keeping fit and maintaining morale. Talented men like Dennis Compton (who played both cricket and football for England) played more games than ever, but for love rather than money.

Cricket continues at Lords.
'I had the feeling that if Goebbels [the Nazi propaganda minister] had been able to broadcast that the war had stopped cricket at Lords it would have been valuable propaganda for the Germans.'

Sir Pelham Warner

▼ *The car parks at the All-England Lawn Tennis Club at Wimbledon being ploughed up for food production.*

REPORTING THE WAR

At 1.50 am on 25 September 1940 the spotters on the roof of the building in which *The Times* newspaper is created throw themselves flat on their faces. Seconds later, a massive bomb rips through the building:

'The Managerial, the Advertisement, the Accounts Departments, and the Intelligence Department and its library, are devastated; the main telephone switchboard and the tape machine are out of action; the rooms that are available are without windows and electric lights, and everywhere files, typewriters and telephones are inextricably mixed among mountains of splintered furniture, wood, plaster and glass. What a scene of devastation! . . . An impossible situation? We shall see.'

From an anonymous diary

Remarkably, *The Times* came out the following day as usual.

▼ *Journalists working as volunteer aircraft spotters on a London rooftop, 1940. The Germans soon stopped daylight raids because their losses were too high.*

▶ *To prevent government interference, newspapers made sure their reporting was as patriotic as possible. Good news, for example, was always given priority over bad.*

Bombing was only one of many problems faced by wartime journalists and reporters. To begin with, there were far too few of them. By 1943 one-third of the nation's journalists were in the armed forces. Many of the others had part-time jobs with the Civil Defence or a similar service. Three-quarters of newspaper photographers had also been called up.

Some 100 journalists became official war correspondents and were sent all over the world to report what was going on. Almost half were killed or wounded.

▲ Government money, which paid for advertising space for propaganda purposes, helped many newspapers keep going during the difficult wartime years.

Those left running newspapers had a frantically difficult time working with unskilled help, teenagers, and old hands who had come back from retirement. The number of pages was reduced. They had to be careful what they said, too: any information that might assist the enemy, such as the name of a ship, was censored by the Government. On several occasions even *HMS Pinafore*, not a ship but the title of a popular opera, was cut out just to be on the safe side!

'Herr Hitler is making a general nuisance of himself. . . . Great upheavals have repercussions in our individual lives. We who are responsible for the preparation and publication of "The Villager" have been caught out by these sadly out-of-joint times; but here we are a little late and only slightly reduced in size.

The Villager, November 1939

'I was taken on by a firm who were doing exhibitions for propaganda – recruiting for the Land Army, and stopping people showing lights at night, and all that sort of thing. It must have been run by the Ministry of Information . . . and . . . they were pretty ghastly paintings.'

Mary Fedden, a propaganda artist during the war

WAR, WORK AND PEACE

Celebrating the news everyone had been longing for – the German surrender – which was signed at midnight on 7 May 1945.

The Government's control and regulation of work achieved its aims. Britain's wartime production of essential goods rose dramatically (see page 17). Scholars now reckon that of all the countries involved in the war, Britain used its resources most effectively and efficiently.

Secondly, the income of most households rose. This was partly because people were working longer hours and partly because many households had two or more incomes. As unemployment fell, between 1938 and 1944 the total of all wages earned rose by 100 per cent. Government taxation, which taxed the rich more heavily than the poor, narrowed the gap between them.

Thirdly, the biggest change was the employment of millions of women. They were often not treated very well by the men they worked with and their pay was usually lower. Jean Wynne, who went to work in a munitions factory in Sheffield, remembers:

'When we went in, it was horrible, because the young chaps who worked there knew very well that any moment they would have to go off to the war. . . . They were mad because they'd been called up. They were mad at us for taking over their jobs, even though we had no choice. They didn't want to show us what to do and they made things really awkward. Never clearly explaining anything.'

However, when the war finished many women wished to remain in work, and this had a notable effect on the post-war world.

For a healthy, happy job

Join the
WOMEN'S LAND ARMY

for details
APPLY TO NEAREST W.L.A. COUNTY OFFICE OR TO W.L.A. HEADQUARTERS 6 CHESHAM PLACE LONDON S.W.1

Women not only worked in factories but also on farms as part of the Women's Land Army.

Fourthly, building on the successes of the wartime government, the Labour government of 1945–51 increased its peacetime power. It nationalised major industries like the railways and electricity, and set up a National Health Service.

ARMY EDUCATION SCHEME
WILL PREPARE YOU FOR YOUR RETURN TO CIVIL LIFE

WHAT CAN YOU DO IN CIVVY ST.?

◀ *Millions of service personnel had to be found jobs when they were allowed to leave the services. Some took advantage of Government education schemes to re-train.*

'*Government and Unions Agree The Northumberland Miners' Association will agree officially to the new National Wages Board . . .*'

Daily Telegraph, 18 May 1943

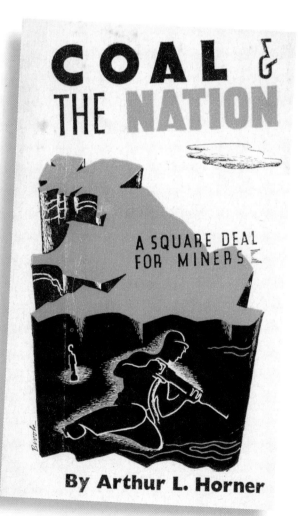

COAL & THE NATION

A SQUARE DEAL FOR MINERS

By Arthur L. Horner

Finally, Churchill's wartime government operated in partnership with trades unions. This was largely Ernest Bevin's work. There were many strikes during the war (2,194 in 1944) but they did not last long. A new partnership had been forged between the Government and the representatives of the workers.

▶ *One battle over, another continues – the coal miners' struggle for fair pay had continued throughout the war and still went on after it was over.*

GLOSSARY

air-raid shelter A place where people could shelter from a bomb attack. Many were underground.

Allies, the Britain, France, the USA, Russia and other countries that fought on the same side in World War Two.

arms Weapons, usually small, hand-held ones.

black-out During the war the Government ordered that all windows had to be covered so that no light showed outside after dark, in case it helped an enemy bomber find its target.

Blitz The heavy bombing of a city. 'Blitz' comes from the German word *blitzkrieg* which means 'lightning war'

brawn Strength.

called up Ordered to join the armed forces or do other war work.

censor To control what is said or shown in a book, film, newspaper, etc, by removing certain words or pictures.

charity An organisation set up to help others, and not make a profit.

Civil Defence The Government's entire organisation of the home front.

civilians Those people not in the armed forces.

conscription An expression which means the same as call up.

decipher To work out the meaning of a secret code.

dole Government pay to those without work.

employee A person employed in a job.

fighter A fast, small aircraft for shooting down other aircraft.

gas mask A mask that fits over the mouth and nose. It filters out poisonous gases in the air.

intellectual An intelligent person interested in ideas.

invade To move into another country by force. In 1940 the Germans invaded France and planned to invade Britain.

jeep A four-wheel drive American car, like a Land Rover. Its name came from the initials GP, which stood for general purpose vehicle.

LDV Local Defence Volunteers, or 'Home Guard', set up in 1940 to defend Britain against invasion.

lathe A machine for shaping wood or metal.

ministry A government department, e.g. the Ministry of Food.

morale People's mood or spirit.

munitions Weapons and ammunition.

nationalise To bring under government control and ownership.

Nazi Party Germany's National Socialist Party. It was led by Adolf Hitler and followed his ideas and wishes.

pacifist A person who does not believe in the use of force.

patriotic Eager to do what is best for one's country.

post-war After the war.

propaganda Information that tries to raise people's spirits or lower the spirits of the enemy.

Quakers A Christian group of people who do not believe in war.

recruit A person who has recently joined a service or job.

shell A bullet, usually large, that explodes when it hits its target.

shift A period of continuous work.

tax Money collected by the Government to run the country.

trades union An organisation that looks after the interests of a particular group of working people.

tribunal A committee or similar group that makes judgements.

voluntary Something one can choose to do – or not.

warden A person who looks after others. An air-raid warden, for example, helped people during air raids.

PROJECTS ON WORK IN WORLD WAR TWO

Make a list of all the jobs you can think of. Divide them into two groups, one essential for the country in time of war, the other non-essential. List the essential jobs in order of importance, and explain your reasons.

Find out what wartime jobs were created in the area where you live. (Did the Land Army work nearby, for example, or were munitions or war vehicles made in a local factory?) Write a sentence or two on each and say whether the work continued after the war.

A project on work during World War Two needs information from various sources. Sources produced at the time of the war are sometimes called *primary* and those produced since that time are sometimes called *secondary*. Some more recent sources of information, mainly books and websites, are listed on the next page. They give mostly other people's views about the war. Sources from the time of war itself are like the quotations in this book. They make a project really interesting and original.

Here are some ways to find primary information:
- Talking to people who lived through the war.
- Looking for objects remaining from the time of the war. These can be large things like buildings. For example, is there an air-raid shelter still standing near you? Smaller objects include steel helmets and gas masks.
- Visiting museums. Most local museums have excellent displays about their area during World War Two. National museums, like the Imperial War Museum in London, are packed with fascinating information.
- Looking at old photographs in family albums.
- Reading printed memories. Your local library will probably have collections made from your area.
- Visit websites that contain primary information, but read the warning on the next page first.

FURTHER INFORMATION

BOOKS TO READ

At Home In World War Two: The Blitz, Stewart Ross (Evans, 2002)
At Home In World War Two: Evacuation, Stewart Ross (Evans, 2002)
At Home In World War Two: Propaganda, Stewart Ross (Evans, 2004)
At Home In World War Two: Rationing, Stewart Ross (Evans, 2002)
At Home In World War Two: Women's War, Stewart Ross (Evans, 2002)
Coming Alive! The Second World War: Dear Mum, I Miss You! Stewart Ross (Evans, 2001)
Coming Alive! The Second World War: I Can Never Go Home Again, Stewart Ross (Evans, 2002)
Coming Alive! The Second World War: What If the Bomb Goes Off? Stewart Ross (Evans, 2001)
History in Writing: The Second World War, Christine Hatt (Evans, 2000)
In Grandma's Day: War, Faye Gardner (Evans, 2000)
Investigating the Home Front, Alison Honey, (National Trust, 1996)
On the Trail of World War II in Britain, Alex Stewart (Watts, 1999)

WEBSITES

Just because information is on the web, it does not mean it is true.

Well-known organisations like the BBC, a university or the Imperial War Museum have sites you can trust. If you are unsure about a site, ask your teacher.

Here are a few useful sites to start from (all are http:// or http://www.):

bbc.co.uk/history/wwtwo.shtml
historyplace.com/worldwar2
iwm.org.uk/lambeth/lambeth.htm

Picture acknowledgements
The following images are courtesy of the Imperial War Museum. Figures following page numbers, where applicable, refer to photograph negative numbers: Cover and imprint page poster, cover (centre): P1233, cover (background): HU73446, title page: D11126, contents page: D8760, p.4 (top): D11129, p.4 (bottom): PST2806, p.5 (top): D4400, p.5 (bottom): D3193, p.6 (top), (bottom): PO290, p.7 (top), p.7 (bottom): D3790, p.8 (top): HU44873, p.8 (bottom): HU36175, p.9 (top), p.9 (bottom): HU50148, p.10 (top): PST0720, p.10 (bottom): D3898, p.11 (top): D4263, p.11 (bottom): PL600213, p.12 (left): PST6389, p.12 (right): D654, p.13 (top): HU36182, p.13 (bottom): D2317, p.14: H5850, p.15 (top): HU50154, p.15 (bottom): HI54933, p.16 (top): PST3757B, p.16 (bottom): P1233, p.17: D672, p.18 (top): D17906, p.18 (bottom): E(MOS)1441, p.19 (top): HU54683, p.19 (bottom): HU74817, p.20 (top): D7681, p.20 (bottom), p.21 (top left): PST2886, p.21 (top middle), p.21 (top right), p.21 (bottom): D3600, p.22: HU36255, p.23 (top): A8530, p.23 (bottom): PL5527, p.24 (top): D23520, p.24 (bottom): D1910, p.26 (top): HU86169, p.26 (bottom): FX3934, p.27: D20483, p.28 (top): HU49482, p.28 (bottom), p.30 (top): PST2955, p.29 (bottom).
Picture on page 25 courtesy of Popperfoto.

Sources of quoted material
Page 7: Cited in Angus Calder, *The People's War Britain 1939-1945*, Pimlico, 1992, p.241.
Page 8: Cited in Angus Calder, *The People's War Britain 1939-1945*, Pimlico, 1992, p.157.
Page 9: Cited in Mavis Nicholson, ed., *What Did You Do In the War, Mummy?* Chatto and Windus, 1995, p.163.
Page 11: Cited in Angus Calder, *The People's War Britain 1939-1945*, Pimlico, 1992, p.197.
Page 13 (top): Cited in Mavis Nicholson, ed., *What Did You Do In the War, Mummy?* Chatto and Windus, 1995, p.151.
Page 13 (bottom): Cited in Raynes Minns, *Bombers and Mash The Domestic Front 1939-45*, Virago, 1999, p.44.
Page 14 (left): Cited in Angus Calder, *The People's War Britain 1939-1945*, Pimlico, 1992, p.124.
Page 14 (right): Cited in Oonagh Hyndman, ed., *Wartime Kent 1939-40*, Meresborough, 1990, p.90.
Page 15: Cited in Raynes Minns, *Bombers and Mash The Domestic Front 1939-45*, Virago, 1999, p.56.
Page 18 (top): Cited in Mavis Nicholson, ed., *What Did You Do In the War, Mummy?* Chatto and Windus, 1995, p.250.
Page 20: Cited in Mavis Nicholson, ed., *What Did You Do In the War, Mummy?* Chatto and Windus, 1995, p.72-3.
Page 21: Cited in Raynes Minns, *Bombers and Mash The Domestic Front 1939-45*, Virago, 1999, p.50.
Page 25: Cited in Angus Calder, *The People's War Britain 1939-1945*, Pimlico, 1992, p.376.
Page 26: Cited from an anonymous diary in *The War Papers*, part 42, PeterWay and Marshall Cavendish, 1977.
Page 27 (top): Cited in A. M. Malin, ed., *The Villager At War*, The Pinner Association, 1995, p.52.
Page 27 (bottom): Cited in Mavis Nicholson, ed., *What Did You Do In the War, Mummy?* Chatto and Windus, 1995, p.55.
Page 28: Cited in Mavis Nicholson, ed., *What Did You Do In the War, Mummy?* Chatto and Windus, 1995, p.203.

INDEX